An Introduction to
Antenna Modelling

Mastering the MMANA-GAL software

by

Steve Nichols, G0KYA

Radio Society of Great Britain

Published by the Radio Society of Great Britain, 3 Abbey Court, Fraser Road, Priory Business Park, Bedford MK44 3WH. Tel 01234 832700 www.rsgb.org

First published 2014

Reprinted 2014, 2016 & 2018

Edited and Layout: Mike Browne, G3DIH
Cover Design: Kevin Williams, M6CYB
Production: Mark Allgar, M1MPA

Printed in Great Britain by Hobbs The Printers Ltd of Totton, Hampshire

ISBN: 9781 9101 9300 6

Contents

Dedication

To my daughters Ellie, M6ELE, and Sarah, M6PUP - the next generation of radio amateurs in the family.

Foreword

I have been using the MMANA-GAL software for a number of years and have found it invaluable. It answers a lot of "what if" questions and saves you making antennas, only to find they don't work as you would like.

MMANA-GAL has also helped explain why some of the antennas I have used have worked better in some directions than others. I well remember an 85-foot W3EDP long-wire that I put up as a stop gap when I first moved into my current property. It cost virtually nothing to make and worked reasonably well. But I noticed that it tended to favour contacts to the south. Once I had mastered MMANA-GAL enough to model the antenna, I was able to see exactly why – the antenna had quite a large radiation lobe out to the south of my property and nothing much anywhere else! It is problems like this that MMANA-GAL can help with, but in my own local club I have found that many radio amateurs have tried to use the software and admitted defeat. This is why the book has been written – not necessarily to make you an MMANA-GAL expert, but to take you through some of the basics and hold your hand as you get used to terms like *Wires*, *Sources* and *Far Field plots*. The net result should be that you can become a competent user of MMANA-GAL, at least able to model single element and simple beam antennas.

The real hero in all of this is Makoto (Mako) Mori, JE3HHT. He wrote the original code, this was then developed further into MMANA-GAL Basic and MMANA-GAL Pro by DL1PBD – Alex Schewelew, and DL2KQ – Igor Gontcharenko. Hats off to all three of you, and the countless others who have produced foreign language versions of MMANA-GAL, or continue to give endless support on the MMANA-GAL Yahoo group.

Steve Nichols, G0KYA/AB8ZV

Introduction to Antenna Modelling

Amateur radio would be a whole lot easier if we could physically see radio waves flowing away from an antenna - that way, we could work out if our antennas were pumping our energy where we wanted it to go. That is, is the RF going in the right direction? What effect is the earth having on the antenna? Or what would happen if we added another element or made one slightly longer? Sadly we can't see these effects with our eyes.

In the early days of antenna design, the methods used were simple – build the antenna, take field strength readings all around it and at a long distance, modify it and see if you have made an improvement.

In the real world antennas interact with other objects and radio waves can bounce around making it difficult to see what you really have. I remember a test on a 2m Yagi beam once that involved me driving two miles down the road and taking comparative readings as it was rotated.

Unfortunately, I found that moving the car just two inches made a massive difference as I was obviously picking up multi-path reflections that interfered with each other, sometimes constructively, sometimes destructively.

Ideally, antennas should be placed in anechoic chambers so that there are no reflections that can disturb the radiation pattern. But if the antenna is the size of a house this becomes impractical. And how many amateurs have anechoic chambers to hand?

In the US much use has been made of antenna testing ranges that are based in the desert to alleviate

Fig 1.1: A US Navy test range showing the arch over the model ship

such problems. A US Navy testing range took another approach and had a huge non-metallic arch (**Fig 1.1**) supporting the transmitting antenna. This was positioned over a 1/48 scale brass model ship on a turntable, all sitting on a copper ground plane under the arch to simulate the electrical characteristics of the sea.

The arch transmitting antenna was positioned by computer control from 0 to 90 degrees in elevation, while the transmitting frequency was also computer controlled.

To compensate for the fact that the models were 1/48 the size of the actual ship, the transmitting frequencies were also increased to 48 times the frequencies of interest.

The net result was that the Navy was able to find the ideal locations for its ship-borne antennas to give the radiation patterns it wanted.

I'm not suggesting that you build a massive model of your house and garden to perform radiation tests – although it would be novel. But nowadays simple computer modelling can give us a better idea of how our antennas are performing and all via a humble Windows-based PC.

Most antenna modelling packages are based on the American Numerical Electromagnetics Code (NEC) program, which is generally credited to Gerald J. Burke and Andrew J. Poggio, of the Lawrence Livermore Laboratories in California, USA.

Fig 1.2: Maxwell equations and three of the field integral solutions that NEC aims to solve

The code development was sponsored by the US Navy and Air Force and was subsequently made publicly available for general use. It has since been distributed for many computer platforms from mainframes to PCs.

NEC is not for the faint hearted. To quote: 'The code is based on the method of moments solution of the electric field integral equation for thin wires and the magnetic field integral equation for closed, conducting surfaces'.

Maxwell's equations

$$\nabla \cdot \mathbf{E} = 0$$

$$\nabla \times \mathbf{E} = -\frac{\partial \mathbf{B}}{\partial t}$$

$$\nabla \cdot \mathbf{B} = 0$$

$$\nabla \times \mathbf{B} = \mu_0 \varepsilon_0 \frac{\partial \mathbf{E}}{\partial t}$$

The Integral Solutions

$$-\frac{j\eta}{4\pi k} \int_{S_1} \vec{J}_s(\vec{r}) \cdot \left[k^2 \hat{s} - \nabla' \frac{\partial}{\partial s} \right] g(\vec{r},\vec{r}') \, dA', \qquad (13)$$

$$\frac{1}{4\pi} \oint_{S_1} \hat{e}_2(\vec{r}) \cdot \left[\vec{J}_s(\vec{r}') \times \nabla' g(\vec{r},\vec{r}') \right] dA', \qquad (14)$$

$$\frac{1}{4\pi} \oint_{S_1} \hat{e}_1(\vec{r}) \cdot \left[\vec{J}_s(\vec{r}') \times \nabla' g(\vec{r},\vec{r}') \right] dA'. \qquad (15)$$

You can read the original NEC documentation at: www.nec2.org/other/nec2prt1.pdf

Needless to say, the original 81-page document is absolutely full of complex equations that the program aims to solve. If your head can take it, I have included Maxwell's equations and the three main equations for the field integral solution for you to ponder.

Maxwell's equations (**Fig 1.2**) have frightened the hell out of every physics student who has ever had to get to grips with them, although they are very elegant, describe how electric and magnetic fields behave, and even show that electromagnetic waves must travel at the speed of light (derived from the way in which magnetic and electric fields permeate free space). The equations for the solutions that NEC uses are even more frightening. You really need to be a post graduate to get very far with them at all.

But luckily, you don't need to be able to understand any of this or how to solve the equations to make the software work!

NEC eventually gave birth to a whole host of derivatives, the most famous one (as far as radio amateurs are concerned) is EZNEC by Roy Lewallen, W7EL. This is really the gold standard for hams, costing $89 for EZNEC v5 and $139 for EZNEC+ v. 5.0.

EZNEC is excellent (we'll take a closer look in a later chapter) and is the subject of the ARRL's book 'Antenna Modelling for Beginners' by Ward Silver, N0AX [1].

But in this book we will take a closer look at a program that is also based on the NEC *engine*, but costs absolutely nothing at all. That program is MMANA-GAL and I have been using it for years. In fact, I haven't really felt the need to upgrade to EZNEC to be honest.

The name MMANA comes from the initials of its creator Macoto Mori ANtenna Analyser (JE3HHT). The GAL part comes from two other hams who have helped develop it further – Igor Goncharenko DL2KQ and Alex Shewelewe DL1PBD.

MMANA-GAL basic is freeware. There are no restrictions on copying or distributing this software as long as the software remains unmodified and JE3HHT's copyright ownership is acknowledged.

As well as English, it is also available in German, French, Bulgarian, Japanese, Spanish, Serbian, Dutch, and Czech languages at the time of writing.

The program has a very active user group at: http://groups.yahoo.com/group/MMANA-GAL where you can get many of your questions answered. The group has more than 600 members who are more than willing to help, plus gives you access to a whole host of antenna modelling definition files and tutorials.

So what can you do with MMANA-GAL? Basically, you can design antennas, check their radiation patterns, check their take-off angles, play with the feed point and optimise the antenna for gain, front-to-back or best SWR match.

It will also show you the antenna's predicted radiation pattern in 3D and has an automatic antenna optimiser with respect to gain, F/B, R+jX (complex impedance), SWR, and current.

Fig 1.3: MMANA-GAL was used to help design my multiband end fed half-wave vertical antenna

I have used it to help design trap dipoles, compare the radiation patterns of magnetic loops with dipoles, and test my end-fed half wave (EFHW) and trapped EFHW vertical antennas (**Fig 1.3**). These latter antennas have proved very popular and are used every year by my local radio club for the International Marconi Day event. I also used MMANA-GAL when testing designs for my book 'Stealth Antennas', which is available from the RSGB.

In this book we will look at how to use MMANA-GAL, how to optimise antennas and see how they perform without cutting a single piece of aluminium tubing or copper wire. I'll show that by moving feed points around in your model you may find the antenna can be made to work on different bands. Or that by orienting your antenna in a certain way it will favour one part of the world over another.

The book will show how you can use MMANA-GAL to design Yagis, quads, loops, verticals and much more. The package comes with a wide range of pre-designed models that you can play with and I also give you some of my own MMANA-GAL designs that feature in the later chapters.

So, all in all, by the time you finish the book you should feel confident about what antenna modelling can do and what it can't. You should also be able to create your own designs and manipulate them to get the results you want.

But a word of warning, an antenna model usually has its limitations, partly because the mathematical model that we have to describe it can almost never be described in the same detail as the real thing (especially its environment and surroundings), and partly because of numerical limitations in the calculating code used.

Most of the time we have to make assumptions about the ground beneath our feet and its electrical characteristics. Also, antenna modelling programs generally don't handle dielectrics very well. A good example of this is modelling an antenna that will ultimately be built using PVC-coated wire. If you don't compensate for the different velocity factor of the wire your antenna will end up having to be a different size to the one you have modelled.

It is also very hard to model ribbon cables, such as 300 or 450 Ohm variants, as you can't easily model the dielectric material (plastic) that holds the two conductors apart.

As someone once said – there is no record of any antenna modelling program actually being used to have a QSO with anyone!

Nevertheless, an antenna modelling program can tell you a lot about what you are building. So with that warning out of the way let's get started.

References

[1] ARRL's book 'Antenna Modelling for Beginners' by Ward Silver, N0AX.

Getting Started With MMANA-GAL

So how do you use MMANA-GAL?

I have run MMANA-GAL on everything from a PC with an Intel Dual Core processor to a small Atom-powered netbook – it doesn't require the latest high-speed processor. However, if you have to perform a calculation on a complex model, a computer with a faster processor will probably be able to handle it more quickly.

You can use the version we have supplied on the CD-ROM or download MMANA-GAL at: *http://hamsoft.ca/pages/mmana-gal.php*

The software will work on PCs running Windows XP, Windows 7 or Windows 8.

Once you have downloaded and installed the software you will notice that it has set up a number of directories.

The root (or MMANA-GAL_Basic) folder contains the main MMANA-GAL program (MMANAGAL_Basic.exe) plus an uninstaller and a few other essential files.

You also have a directory called **Language**, which contains the various foreign language files. You don't need to touch this. The **Help** folder contains the files needed (in English and Russian) when you access *help* from the drop-down menu in MMANA-GAL. Again, you don't need to touch this, although clicking on the file called index.htm will open the help file in your default internet browser should you wish to view it without running the main program.

Finally, you have a folder called **ANT**, which contains many sub folders, each crammed with a host of '.MAA' antenna definition files for you to play with. We will take a look at these later.

Getting started

Having installed the software you can now start the program by double clicking on the *MMANA-GAL_Basic.exe* file or by using the shortcut that should have been set up.

Understanding Wires, Loads and Sources

There are a few terms you need to know before you get going. Firstly, your MMANA-GAL antenna design is made up of straight **Wires**. Then we can include **Loads** (made up of inductors (L) and/or capacitors (C), eg traps/loading coils). Once this is built we then apply a **Source** of a specific impedance at a point on one of the wires. Think of the source as the point where you would normally connect your coax or other feed line.

Wires is a bit of a misnomer as the 'wire' can be just that, made from copper, aluminium or iron, or a pipe/tubing made out of copper, aluminium or iron. You can even design your own *user* pipe or wire material. If modelling tubing you can even define a taper.

Selecting the correct feed impedance

We can also choose the input impedance that we wish to match to. That is, we can design an antenna and test it just as if we were connecting it to 50 ohm coax. Or we can adjust the impedance by going to *Setup* and changing it to what we want.

If you do that (in the Standard Z (SWR=1) box) **Fig 2.1** you will see that you are offered values for 28, 50, 75, 112, 300, 400 and 600 Ohms. One quick tip, if you want a value different to this, say 450 Ohms as you are modelling a vertical that uses a 9:1 Unun, just go ahead and type in 450 Ohms and press 'OK'. You can do the same for 200 Ohms, which is useful when modelling antennas with 4:1 baluns.

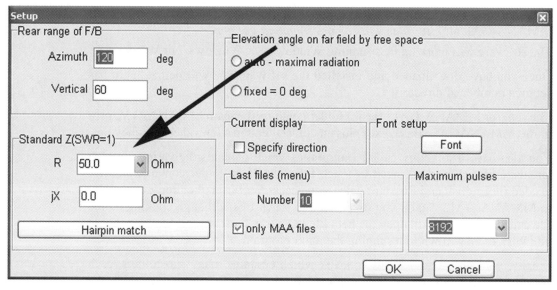

Fig 2.1:
Make sure you have selected the correct impedance

You will now see in the 'Calculate' tab that the SWR value has changed to 'SWR 450'. That is, MMANA-GAL is calculating the SWR and impedance as if the antenna were connected to a 450 Ohm output.

So let's get started

As an easy introduction to MMANA-GAL we are going to start off by using one of the supplied .MAA files that comes with the package.

This is going to be a 20m half wave dipole.

So if it isn't running, go ahead and start MMANA-GAL. The program should run.

From now on, any term in bold refers to one of the four tabs that appear in MMANA-GAL – Geometry, View, Calculate and Far field plots.

Now select File >> Open (*.maa) and navigate to the 'MMANA-GAL\ANT\HF simple\Dipole\' folder and select 'DP20.maa' **Fig 2.2**. This file was originally saved with a default frequency of 14.05MHz.

Press Open.

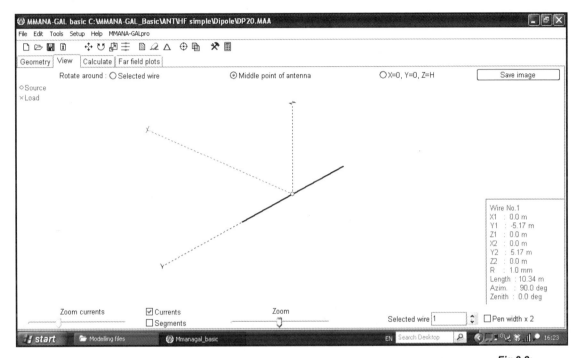

You may now be in the **View** tab (**Fig 2.2**), if not click on it and you should see the dipole in free space. Clicking and dragging somewhere on the screen will allow you to rotate the dipole and even look at it from underneath. Note that it is sitting on a dotted framework that shows it is oriented in the Y plane, with the X plane going off at 90 degrees and the Z plane going vertically.

This is a standard orthogonal view – get used to it as you will be seeing a lot more of it and we will be describing your own antennas in terms of their X, Y and Z coordinates.

You may also notice that there is a small red blob in the centre of the dipole. This is the feed point where we are going to apply our source. Remember what I said earlier, think of the source as the point where you would normally connect your coax or feed line.

On the right of the screen you will see a box that describes what we have – a single 10.34m long wire (Wire No. 1) that stretches from -5.17m on the Y axis to +5.17m That is, a single piece of wire representing a half wave dipole for 20m.

Now select the **Geometry** tab. You will see that the name of the antenna design is 'Dipole 20m' **Fig 2.3**. You can change this is you wish. I recommend that any design you make is given a name as it makes it easier for you to identify what you have built in the future.

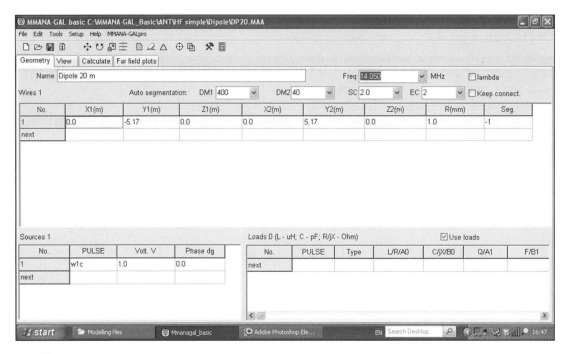

Fig 2.3:
Here is where you can 'build' your antennas using 'wires'. We also add our feed point 'Source' and any loading coils/traps

From the top, you can see that the design frequency is 14.05MHz. Ignore the fields marked 'Auto segmentation' for now.

In the 'Wires 1' matrix you can see the definition for our dipole, again showing that it is a single wire stretching from -5.17m to +5.17m on the Y axis. The radius of the wire is 1mm.

This is important as all of our antenna designs will be built up from single pieces of wire. You can't have circles or curves so everything has to be made with straight wires.

Don't worry too much as it is possible to build 'round' designs, such as octagonal magnetic loops, using a multitude of wires to form a circle.

Staying on the **Geometry** tab, at the bottom left is a box marked 'Sources 1'. Note in the PULSE box it says 'w1c' This shows that we are applying a single source (think of it as a single feed point) to the antenna and we are applying it at the centre of wire 1.

The term 'w1c' merely means apply the source to 'wire one centre'. Ignore the Voltage applied (which defaults to 1V) and the phase.

Our other options could be feeding the centre of a second wire (if we had one) in which case we would specify w2c, feeding it at the beginning (w2b) or feeding it at the end (w2e).

To recap:

- The beginning of wire one would be 'w1b'

- The centre of wire two would be 'w2c'

- The end of wire three would be 'w3e'.

Now, on the right is a box marked *Loads*, this is where we might apply loading coils and/or capacitors (perhaps to form a trap, such as we would use in a trap dipole).

For this antenna we don't have any loads so it is left blank, but if we wanted to we would use the same system as earlier to describe what wire and where they would be applied eg w1c, w2e, w3e etc.

Now, move over to the **Calculate** tab (**Fig 2.4**), make sure that the frequency of 14.050MHz is selected. Also make sure that you have selected *Real* as the ground and that you have selected 10m metres in 'add height' and material 'Cu wire'.

If we don't select 'Real' as the ground the program will assume we are testing the antenna in free space – useful if we were designing an antenna for interplanetary use, but not much use if the antenna is in our back garden!

The default values for the ground setup are dielectric constant '13' and conductivity '5'. I suggest you leave these alone unless you actually know precisely what values your earth actually has. We will look at that later.

Likewise, we need to select the correct *Material* as copper is a better conductor than aluminium, which in turn is a better conductor than iron.

Now press the 'Start' button at the bottom left of the window. MMANA-GAL will quickly calculate how the antenna would work at this frequency.

The antenna's impedance and SWR will be calculated, based on the frequency of 14.050MHz.

The results show a resistance of 74.81 Ohms (R), a reactance of -20.43 Ohms (jX) and a SWR (relative to 50 Ohms) of 1.68:1.

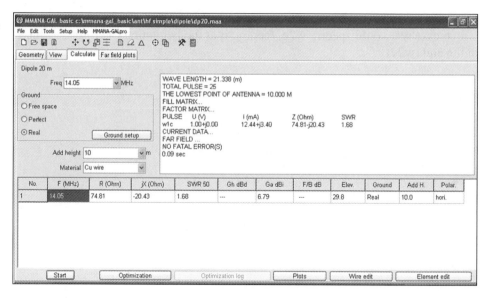

If you are new to antenna theory ignore the resistance/reactance boxes and concentrate on the SWR. But, if you are an antenna expert the complex impedance (resistance and reactance) boxes will also tell you whether the reactance is capacitive or inductive (+ or -).

Anyway, back to the SWR, 1.68:1 is not a bad match to our 50 Ohm coaxial cable, but this only tells us part of the story. Looking along the line we also see that the antenna has a maximum gain of 6.79dB relative to an isotropic source (dBi) and the maximum occurs at 29.8 degrees to the horizontal over real ground.

To see the far field pattern plots, select the **Far Field Plots (Fig 2.5)** tab at the top, where the Azimuth and Elevation radiation plots are displayed.

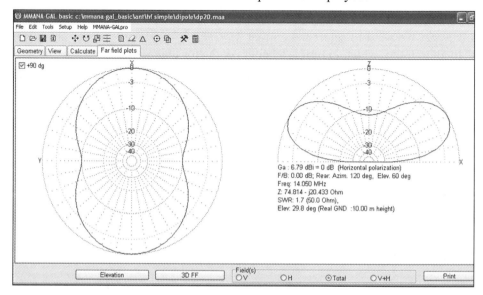

A quick word of warning – **the azimuth plot shown on the left (Fig 2.5) is that calculated for the elevation angle of maximum radiation, in this case 29.8 degrees**. If you want to know how well your antenna performs at another angle, say 10 degrees if you want to work DX, you need to go to the 'Elevation' button and select your new angle.

If you put in 10 degrees at this stage you will see that the left-hand azimuth pattern shrinks dramatically. This is probably one of the most common mistakes people make when first using MMANA-GAL. If you don't select the radiation angle that you wish to inspect you can be fooled into thinking that your azimuth pattern and gain are better than they actually are. If you are confused about azimuth and elevation, think of the left-hand plot (azimuth) as being what you would see if you looked down on the antenna from above. The right-hand plot (elevation) is what you would see if you looked from the side.

For example, the maximum gain of this 20m dipole antenna when mounted at 10m is 6.8dBi when measured at 29.8 degrees. However, change the elevation angle to 10 degrees and you will see that it goes down to 1.5dBi.

A quick tip: you can quickly see what your gain is at all sorts of angles by clicking and dragging on the right-hand elevation view of the radiation pattern. You will see a red dot appear on the plot and you can now move this up and down by holding your mouse button down. For example, at 20 degrees elevation you will see that the gain is now 5.8dBi (reading it off the top centre of the screen). You can also use the same trick by clicking on the left-hand azimuth plot and seeing what the gain is at various azimuth angles. If you know how your antenna will finally be oriented (say the Y axis represents North-South) you can quickly see how well it will radiate in all directions.

If you now also click on the **3D FF** (three dimensional far field) button (**Fig 2.6**) you can see how the antenna radiation pattern looks in three dimensions. Again, by clicking and dragging you can rotate the 3D plot to see what it looks like from any angle.

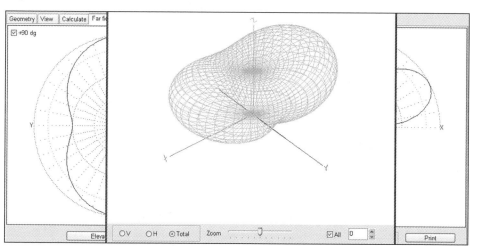

Fig 2.6:
You can also view the far field plots in three dimensions (3D)

Now, close the 3D window and select the **Calculate** tab again to return to that window and change the 'Freq' by typing to 14.175MHz – the middle of the 20m amateur band – and press the Start button again.

The window will now display the new values at this frequency eg A resistance of 75.86 Ohms (R), a reactance of -7.727 Ohms (jX) and an SWR (relative to 50 Ohms) of 1.54:1.

That's a better match than we had before – which is no surprise considering the antenna is cut for the centre of the band, not the CW end down at 14.050MHz.

But if we really want to see what the antenna is doing in terms of its SWR values across the whole band MMANA-GAL can do that for us too. From the **Calculate** tab just select 'Plots' (**Fig 2.7**) at the bottom of the screen. This will open up a new window showing you the Far Field plot again.

Now click to the SWR tab, where you will see a grid and a blank screen.

At the top right of the window is a box marked 'BW'. This defines the bandwidth that we are about to calculate the SWR for, based on our centre calculated frequency, which should now be 14.175MHz.

The default 400kHz is fine, so go ahead and press 'Detailed'. Within a few seconds you should now have a detailed plot of the predicted SWR values for the antenna in the range 13.975MHz to 14.375MHz.

You can see that the SWR minimum is a little higher in frequency than 14.175MHz meaning the antenna is just a little too short, However, the SWR is below 1.8:1 across the whole band so it is nothing to worry about.

If you now want to play with the design, changing the length of the antenna to 10.39m (Y=-5.19m and +5.19m) will give you the desired SWR minimum at 14.175MHz.

Fig 2.7: You can also get MMA-NA-GAL to plot the predicted SWR across the band

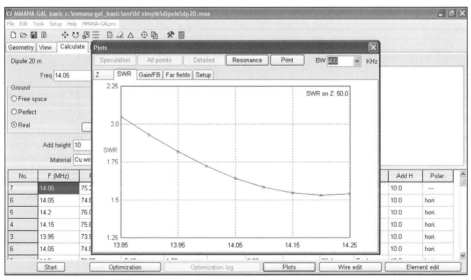

You might also want to play with changing the height of the dipole to see what effect this has on the radiation pattern and SWR.

For example, changing the height to 20m (by going to **Calculate** (**Fig 2.7**) and changing the 'add height' to 20m and then pressing start) will result in a very different radiation pattern with additional lobes. Note that the SWR changes very slightly too.

The peak gain (7 dBi) is now at 14.8 degrees instead of 28.8 degrees, showing that getting your dipole higher can result in improved lower angle radiation.

In a later chapter I'll show how to make these comparisons much easier.

But above all, remember, this is a model. The actual results you get when you put up a real antenna in your back garden will vary dramatically as the SWR will depend upon its height above ground, its proximity to other objects (including houses and trees) and even its material.

As I said earlier, if you construct your dipole out of PVC-coated wire it will physically end up having to be shorter than calculated to compensate for its different velocity factor.

The velocity factor (VF) denotes the speed at which an electromagnetic sig nal passes through the wire, relative to the speed of light. As this velocity is lower than the speed of light in dielectric-covered wires it can make the wire 'look' electrically longer. That is, when you finally make, rather than model, your antenna the actual wire lengths could be just 90-95% of the length MMANA-GAL calculated.

For example, if MMANA-GAL has calculated that you need a wire one metre long, and you use PVC-coated wire with a VF of 0.94, you will find that your wire only actually needs to be 94cm long to work.

Now, the late Reg G4FGQ once wrote: "With ordinary antenna wire, insulated up to twice the wire diameter with PVC, the reduction in velocity from the speed of light is insignificant and pruning can be forgotten about. It is much less than the pruning sometimes done for end effect which is usually unnecessary anyway".

So what are you supposed to do? Best advice is build the antenna using the MMANA-GAL calculated measurements. If it works as it should, great. But if you find that the resonant frequency is lower than you wanted you may have to start pruning, reducing each element length by the same percentage until you get to where you need to be.

Most of the antennas I have built with PVC-coated wire after modelling them in MMANA-GAL have had to be shortened. Whether this was due to the velocity factor of the wire, end effects, or the antenna's interaction with the environment makes no difference in reality – they had to be shortened from the calculated values.

Finally, MMANA-GAL only offers a guide to what will happen in real life with your antenna, albeit a very good guide. But if you take the MMANA-GAL model, build it in real-life and place it in a domestic environment, you may need to tweak the design slightly to get the optimum results.

Building an Antenna from Scratch

In the last chapter we took an existing design from the MMANA-GAL collection, analysed it and then made a change to its length and height to see what affect it had. In this chapter we will build an antenna from scratch, which will give you a better idea of how to build your own designs with MMANA-GAL.

We are going to build a 40m full-size loop antenna. That is, a square horizontal loop antenna that is around 40m in circumference. The aim is to use it on 7MHz (the 40m band). After building it we can play with the frequency to see what SWR values we get on other bands.

So, first we need to plan what we are building. The loop will have four sides, each of equal length.

To calculate the rough overall length in metres take 300 and divide by the frequency, which is 7.1MHz. This gives us a total length of 42.24m, or four sides of length 10.56m.

What we are going to do is build the antenna by plotting the X, Y and Z coordinates of each of the ends of the four wires. To make life easy we will ignore the Z direction, and only plot the X and Y points.

So let's get building. Firstly, if you haven't already started MMANA-GAL do so now. Now go to: **File >>New** to create the new antenna. We can start by giving it a name in the **Geometry** tab (**Fig 3.1**). Go ahead by clicking in the 'Name' box and then typing '40m full size horizontal loop'. While you are there change the frequency to 7.1MHz in the box next to it.

Now we go to the wires section and click in the first box marked 'X1(m)'. In here we input '0' and press return. You will notice that MMANA-GAL automatically puts in the additional information along the line. Now we can go back and edit it. Start by clicking and adding '10.56' in the X2(m) box and press return. Congratulations, you have added the first wire.

To add the second, click on the X1(m) box in the row marked 'Next' and press return. Once again it will auto-complete the whole row. Add 10.56m to the X1(m) box. Now for the other end of the wire we enter '10.56' in the Y1(m) box and press **Enter**. We also have to put '10.56' in the X2(m) box, otherwise we will end up with a diagonal wire.

The third wire has its starting points at the end of the second wire so X1(m)=10.56 and Y1(m)= 10.56. But this time the end points are at X2(m)=0 and Y2(m) = 10.56.

Finally, the fourth wire starts at X1(m)=0 and Y1(m)=10.56. The end points are X2(m)=0 and Y2(m)=0.

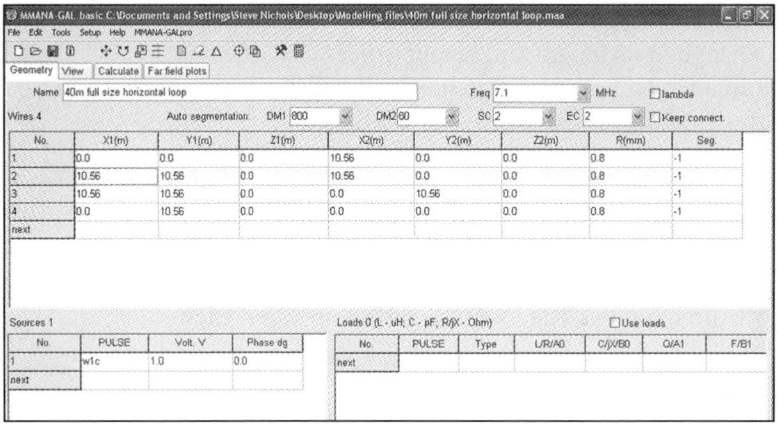

Fig 3.1:
Here is what your Geometry tab should look like when the loop is complete

Having completed that, if you go to the **View** tab (**Fig 3.2**) you will see that you have created a complete square, with all of the points connecting. Now go back to the **Geometry** tab (**Fig 3.1**).

At this point we have to add a 'Source' for our feed point. We want to put it halfway along the first wire. Do you remember how we do that?

We need to put 'w1c' in the 'PULSE' box in the 'Source' section. So go ahead and do that now, pressing enter when complete. All done? OK, now go to the **View** tab and you will see a small red blob where we have placed the feed point source. At this stage you will see that one of the wires is bolder than the others. This is because it has been selected. Click on another and you will see that it now becomes bold. At the same time the box on the lower right shows which wire has been selected and its coordinates. This can be useful when trying to work out what you have done wrong in building your design.

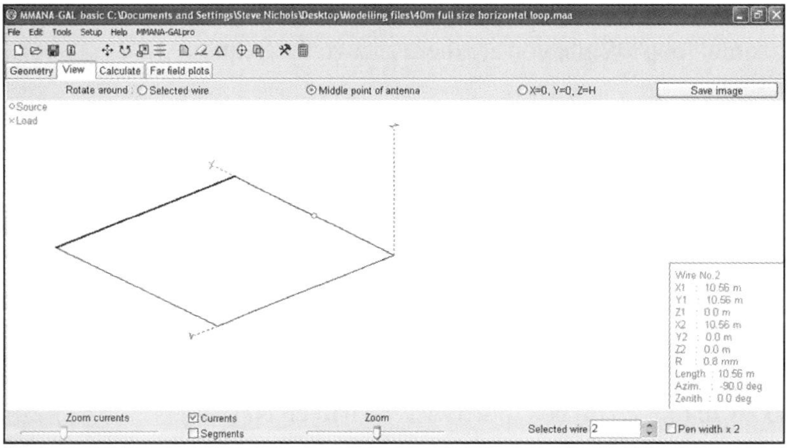

Fig 3.2:
The completed 40m square loop as seen in the View tab

Now we can go to the **Calculate** tab (**Fig 3.3**). Make sure that you select 'Real' for the Ground and also add 20m to the 'add height' box. The material should also be set to 'Cu wire'.

At this stage we should save our design in case the computer crashes – it does happen! So go to 'File >> Save as ...(*.maa)' and give the design a name and save location. I tend to save my designs in 'My antennas' folder. Let's call it '40mloop' – the program will automatically add the .maa extension.

If you are really stuck at this stage, I have supplied a completed MMANA-GAL file for the loop called '40m full size horizontal loop.maa'.

Now, making sure we have the 'Freq' set as 7.1MHz we can press 'Start'. After a second or so you will see that the SWR is calculated as 8.52:1 – this is quite normal.

The reality is that the impedance of a full-sized loop is not 50 Ohms, but more like 100 Ohms, but let's see if we can improve the match first before we start looking at alternative ways of feeding it.

First, go to the 'Plots' tab under **Calculate** and select 'SWR' (**Fig 3.3**). Now, press the 'Resonance' button, which will automatically show us where the antenna is actually resonant and exhibits the lowest SWR. Technically, the resonant point of an antenna is where the reactance is zero, but for this demonstration we will presume that the resonant point and the lowest SWR are at the same frequency.

You will see that the graph tells us that the resonant point is actually about 7.538 MHz. This is higher than the desired 7.1MHz. In other words, our antenna is too short.

MMANA-GAL can actually automatically work out what adjustments are needed to your antenna to make it resonant, but we will look at that option in a later chapter. In the meantime, change all the lengths from 10.56m to 11.2m and run the program again by pressing 'Start'.

You'll see that the SWR is now down to 2.6:1 and if we go to the 'Plots >> SWR' tab and then press 'Resonance' the SWR minimum is now at 7.116MHz – that's near enough to 7.1MHz for us.

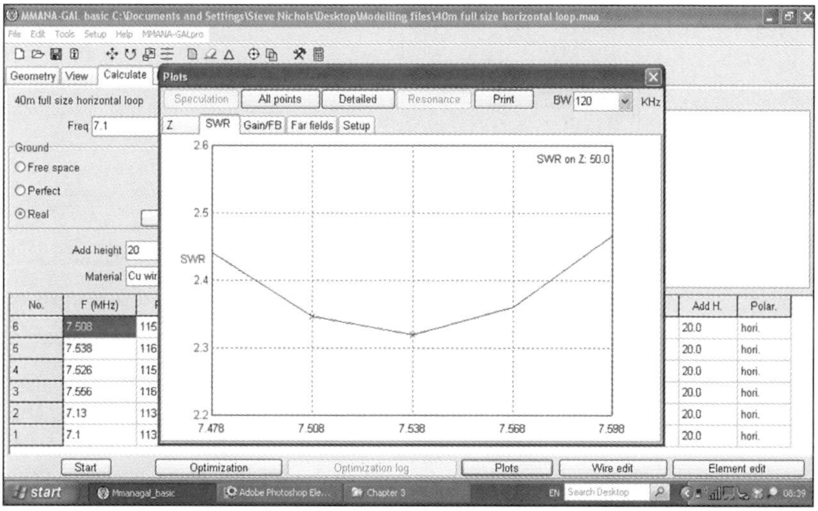

But the SWR is 2.63:1 and this is because the impedance of the full-wave loop is more like 130 Ohms than 50 Ohms at this height of 20m. Change the height to 10m and run the program and you will see that the SWR is now about 4.81:1 and the resonance point has been lowered to 6.84MHz from 7.116MHz.

Fig 3.3: The loop, when mounted at a height of 20m, is actually resonant on about 7.538MHz

This shows us that the formula of 300/frequency to give the length of an antenna is only a guide as the ultimate length will depend on many factors, including the height above ground.

So can MMANA-GAL help us to understand how best to match our antenna to 50 Ohm coax? Well, yes it can.

One solution is to feed the antenna with a 4:1 balun (**Fig 3.4**) to better match it to our 50 Ohm coax. To model this in MMANA-GAL we need to change the feed impedance to 200 Ohms (4 x 50 Ohms).

To do this go to 'Setup' in the top menu and select 'Setup'. Now click in the box marked 'R' in Standard Z (SWR=1) and type in '200' and press enter. Now click OK. At this point you will see that the calculated SWR has changed to 1.81:1 (at 7.1MHz) and the column heading is SWR 200 to remind us that we are not dealing with 50 Ohms any more.

Fig 3.4:
Adding a 4:1
balun at the
feed point
brings the SWR
down nicely

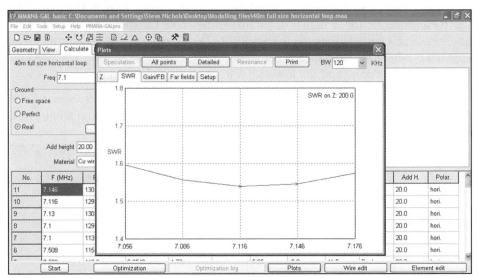

That's better, and to be honest, at the end of a length of coax you would find that the SWR would actually be lower than 1.81:1, thanks to the losses. It would probably be below 1.5:1.

But now that we have added the balun (by changing the feed or source impedance to 200 Ohms) we can also quickly check to see what the SWR would be on other bands. So, go ahead, and in the **Calculate** tab change the frequency to 14.150MHZ and press 'Start'. You'll quickly see that the SWR is now 2.45:1 (if using a 4:1 balun, 200 Ohms and a height of 10m).

On 21.2MHz the SWR would be 2.77:1, and on 28.2MHz it would be 3.38:1. I will let you play with other frequencies, such as 10.12, 18.1 and 24.9MHz.

What you quickly discover is that a 40m full-wave loop at a height of 10m gives a reasonable match to 50 Ohm coax on 40, 20, 15 and 10m as long as you use a 4:1 balun. But it doesn't give a very good match on the other bands. If you want to use it as a multi-band antenna you are better feeding it with open wire feeder into a balanced ATU.

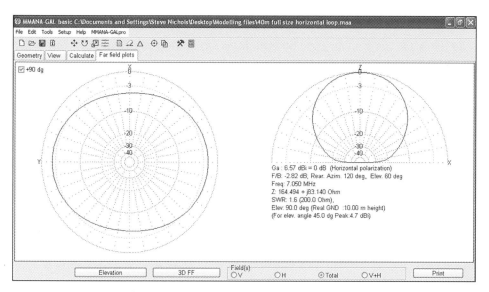

Fig 3.5:
The Far Field plot shows that the radiation on 40m with the antenna at 10m is nearly all skyward

MMANA-GAL will also show us that: The radiation pattern of a full wave horizontal loop on 40m (**Fig 3.5**) is nearly all high-angle if we mount it at 10m, but gets lower if we mount it at 20m. At a height of 10m it would work well for contacts around the country using NVIS (Near Vertical Incidence Skywave) radiation. But if you want to work DX with it the antenna will have to be mounted higher – even at 20m height the maximum angle of radiation is still about 50 degrees to the horizontal.

The radiation pattern on the higher bands can break up into a multi-lobe pattern. On 20m, when mounted at 10m for example, you get a four-leaf clover pattern (if you look down on the antenna) (**Fig 3.6**) with maximum radiation at about 28 degrees elevation. This could be a reasonably efficient DX antenna – as long as the station you wish to work is on a lobe!

Fig 3.6:
On 20m the loop breaks up into four lobes with lower angle radiation

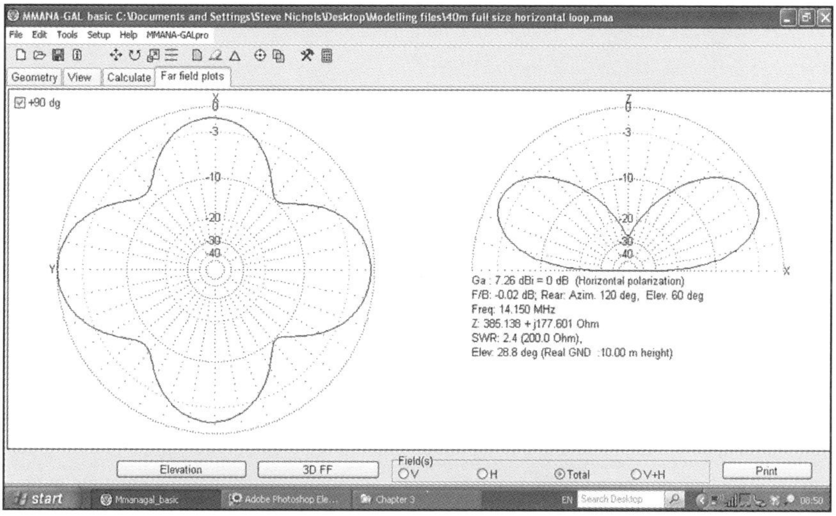

On 10m it again becomes a very high angle radiator and not suited to DX. Try it and see, by changing the 'Freq' in the **Calculate** tab.

But the exciting thing is that we have found all this out by just using the MMANA-GAL software. We haven't had to build a thing.

So in this chapter we have learned:

- How to create an antenna by building a structure using 'Wires'.
- How to place our 'Source' on the wire we want and how to put it at the beginning, centre or end of the wire.
- How to check the SWR and also find the resonant point of the antenna.
- How to then adjust the length of each wire manually to bring the SWR down.
- How to simulate the effect of using a 4:1 balun and see its effect on the SWR.
- How to look at the calculated SWR points and Far Field Plots on different bands to see whether the antenna is performing the way we would like it to.
- How to move the antenna higher or lower and see what effect it has on the radiation pattern.

In the next chapter we will look at some of the more advanced tools within MMA-NA-GAL.

Advanced MMANA-GAL Usage

In this chapter I want to explore some of the more advanced featured within MMANA-GAL and also look at some tricks and tips that will make it easier for you to design antennas.

Make sure you put the source on a straight wire

This may not seem obvious, but some say it is best practice when using MMANA-GAL that when placing a source onto your antenna design it is important to put it on a straight wire, be it vertical or horizontal.

This is easy enough if you are designing a horizontal dipole, but if you are creating an inverted V, or any antenna where the wires meet at an angle you have to take some additional steps.

The easiest way to do this is to add a short length of horizontal wire between the sloping elements and add the source to the centre of that wire. This means that you may have to fiddle with the X,Y, and Z coordinates a little to make room for the wire, but in most cases this will make little difference to the design.

For example, adding a short section of wire (say 5cm long) to the centre of an 80m inverted V will make no difference whatsoever to the overall result you obtain.

I did a back-to-back test on a 40m (**Fig 4.1**) Inverted V design and it seemed to make no difference whether I added a short length of wire between the elements on which to place the source, or just had two wires that met at an angle and then placed the feed point at the end of one of the them. But I mention this as it does seem to appear in a lot of designs, especially where you may have

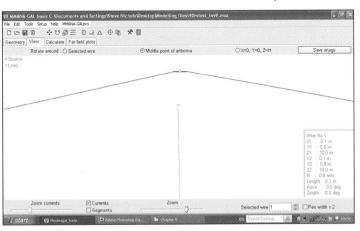

Fig 4.1: Add your source to a straight piece of wire, not at an acute junction

perhaps two sets of dipoles coming to a central feed point. Then it makes sense to connect both pairs with a short wire.

Basic Pythagoras (for dealing with inverted Vs and slopers)

Working with horizontal and vertical antennas is all well and good, but in the real world we often have to deal with sloping wires, such as found with inverted V antennas.

Then you may get a problem – trying to work out the X, Y and Z coordinates of a sloping wire. In this case I find that Pythagoras comes to the rescue. For example, say you have one half of a 40m half-wave dipole that is 10.7m long. If placed in free space its coordinates might be X1(m)=0, Y1(m)=0, Z1(m)=0, X2(m)=10.7, Y2(m)=0, Z2(m)=0. This is actually hard to visualise, but put it into MMANA-GAL and it will all make sense.

So what happens if the wire is supported 10m high at the apex and slopes down to 3m at the end? What now?

Fig 4.2:
Use Pythago-
ras' theorem
to work out the
coordinates of
sloping wires

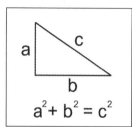

Well, Pythagoras Theorem (**Fig 4.2**) helps us work out the new coordinates.

The first set of coordinates are easy – X1(m)=0, Y1(m)=0, Z1(m)=10

But what we have is a right-angled triangle with a hypotenuse length of 10.7m, the short side (height) of 7m. So what is the length of the longer side?

Well Pythagoras says (if you can remember school days) that the square of the hypotenuse equals the sum of the squares of the two adjacent sides.

So in the case $10.7^2 = 7^2 + x^2$

So, $114.49 = 49 + x^2$

Or $x^2=65.49$ (taking 49 away from 114.49)

Therefore x = 8.09m (taking the square root of 65.49).

If you don't have a scientific calculator that can handle square roots don't panic. In MMANA-GAL go to Tools >> Calculator and you can access the built-in one for Windows, which can handle square roots (look out for the sqrt button on the XP version or the '√' symbol in Windows 7).

So this means that the end point of our dipole leg will be 8.09m from the mast supporting the other end (if that helps you visualise it).

So, with a deep breath, we can now say that the full coordinates of our piece of wire are: X1(m)=0, Y1(m)=0, Z1(m)=10, X2(m)=8.09, Y2(m)=0, Z2(m)=3.

Phew! The other leg is now quite easy as it is just a mirror image of the first one, with the X2(m) coordinate becoming -8.09m. If you want to add a short piece of straight wire to the middle for your feed point just set the points for Wire 1 to

X1(m) to 0.01m and for Wire 2 to X2(m) to -0.01m. This additional piece of wire, which is only 2cm long, will make little difference to the overall SWR figures.

Now, if this has left your head in a spin bear in mind that a multi-element antenna with lots of angled wires can become a bit of nightmare to build, but if you draft it out on paper first and carefully calculate all the coordinates first it does become easier to put into MMANA-GAL. I find that once I have added more than about four elements I lose track of what I am trying to do, so a rough diagram of what you are trying to produce might work wonders for you.

You usually know if you have made a mistake as the predicted SWR comes out as 1999999:1! A sure sign that you have a 'break' somewhere and your coordinates don't line up. But if you can't handle Pythagoras (or trigonometry for that matter, which can be useful if you know that one leg of the dipole must slope down at, say, 30 degrees) there is another more visual way to design inverted Vs. I don't find it as accurate, but it might work for you.

Using the 'Wire Edit' function

Hidden away in MMANA-GAL's 'Edit' menu is an option called 'Wire Edit' (**Fig 4.3**). This provides a visual way of adding wires into MMANA-GAL and is fairly easy to use once you get used to it.

With 'Wire edit' you get three main tool icons (centre right) – 'Edit Wire', 'New Wire' and 'New Loop'. To try it out, try selecting the centre 'New Wire' option and then clicking and dragging on the screen to draw your wire.

You can zoom in or out to take a closer look at what you are doing and once you have drawn them you can tell which one is selected as it is highlighted in red.

The box at the top right is helpful as it gives you the coordinates of the wire, but more importantly it gives you the wire length. So if you are designing inverted V elements you don't have to worry about Pythagoras as MMANA-GAL automatically determines the length of the wire, even if it is at an angle.

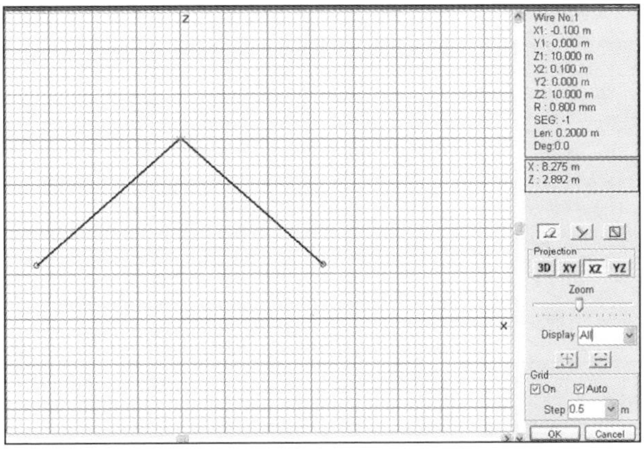

The grid helps you place the wires accurately, plus you can alter the scale of the grid for finer work by using the 'Step' command. It also gives you the opportunity to work in a 'flat sheet' mode using the XY,

*Fig 4.3:
Using the wire edit function can make life a lot easier*

XZ or YZ options, or you can select 3D to see what your design looks like in real life.

All the time you are adding or adjusting wires, MMANA-GAL is busy working in the background updating the details in the **Geometry** tab. You can then add a Source and away you go, working as usual in the **Calculate** tab.

I find the 'Wire edit' option a little fiddly, but if you not entirely sure what lengths your antenna elements should be it is a quick and easy way to make changes and it can be visually easier than editing the X, Y, Z coordinates.

If you want to see 'Wire edit' in action Callum M0MCX has a few interesting You-Tube videos that show it very well.

Go to *http://www.youtube.com/watch?v=XlWNXJEB6ps*

Callum has a number of other videos that show MMANA-GAL in action, In fact YouTube is a mine of information on MMANA-GAL – when I last checked, searching for 'MMANA-GAL' came up with more than 200 videos.

This is probably one of the easiest ways to learn what MMANA-GAL can do.

Optimising the design

If you don't quite get the result you want with MMANA-GAL you can always fiddle with the length of each wire to try and improve it. This works, but there is also an automated way of optimising your antenna design.

For example, earlier I made a 40m inverted V design that had legs that were 10.7m long. This gave a calculated SWR on 7.05MHz of 2.31:1, with a low of about 1.32:1 at 6.851MHz.

Let's say, as an example, that I actually wanted the antenna to be resonant at 7.1MHz. Obviously, the antenna needs to be shorter, but by how much?

Fig 4.4:
The optimisa-
tion tool makes
it easier to get
the results you
want

I could start to play around with the antenna length by adjusting the values in the Geometry tab. Or I could use 'Wire edit', but that is quite slow and tedious. So is there a way to make MMANA-GAL work out the best length for the antenna? Well, yes there is by using the 'Optimization' option (**Fig 4.4**) at the bottom of the Calculate tab.

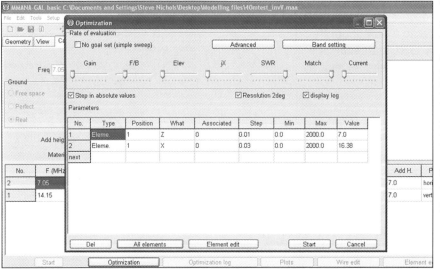

This gives us the opportunity to optimise the antenna design in terms of its Gain, Front-to-Back ratio, Elevation angle (maximum radiation), Reactance (jX), SWR, Match or Current. These last two are not of much relevance for us.

You get to choose what priority you want to focus on by using a set of sliders. That is, if you want to optimise the SWR then move that slider to the right and move the others to the left. Likewise, if designing a beam for the maximum front-to-back ratio move that slider to the right and leave the others set left. In the real world you might want to optimise the front to back while maintaining a low SWR so you could use a combination of the 'F/B' slider and the 'SWR'.

But before we go any further, a word of caution. The optimisation routine will do its best, but some times the end result doesn't fit in with your real-world requirements. For example, I once tried to work out what the best length would be for a reflector under an 80m dipole to maximise the gain straight upwards for NVIS contacts. After running the routine it came up with an answer, but I hadn't said I also wanted to keep the SWR low, so I ended up with an antenna that had lots of sky gain, but was completely useless if you wanted to connect it to coax.

To a large extent it is a case of using the tool properly. You can specify what frequency you wish to optimise for and also what you are prepared to change, in terms of the X, Y and Z values of the variables. But you might not always like the result you get.

As Alistair NH7O says in his tutorial on using the optimisation routine on the internet (at https://sites.google.com/a/wildblue.net/nh7o/mmana-gal-antenna-analysis/optimization-part1): 'Is this the best possible solution? Not necessarily. The best way to visualize the process is to think of a terrain that is comprised of rolling hills. The area of this hilly terrain symbolizes the complete set of all possible antennas, with the height of any hill indicating the degree of conformance with the desired goal.

'The optimization routine wanders around this terrain, looking for the highest hill. But it may find a lesser hill, and home in on that local peak instead. This is where some experience and intuition on the part of the antenna designer is needed to decide if things could be better or not.

'Restarting the algorithm with a different initial condition can be sufficient to set the search path in an entirely different direction. However, in the present case, the algorithm does very well.'

Indeed it does. Using the optimisation routine on our 40m inverted V di-

Fig 4.5: After MMANA-GAL has finished you will have a better match

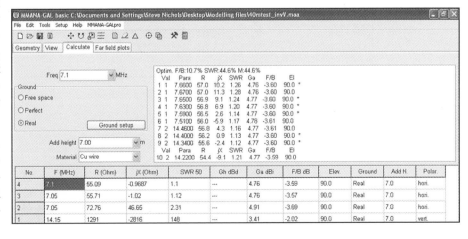

pole shows (**Fig 4.5**) that to be resonant on 7.1MHz the antenna legs need to be 10.386m long, not 10.7m. It also calculated the best angle between the legs of the dipole – the legs needed to be slightly closer together to bring the SWR down.

The end result was a low SWR of 1.1:1 at 7.1MHz – and all done by pressing a few buttons! Comparing the far field plots for both the original design and the optimised design showed that they were virtually identical, so MMANA-GAL had managed to come up with a better match without disturbing the plot – very clever!

You also have an advanced option in the Optimization routine that allows you to set target goals, such as a gain of x dB or an SWR of, say 1:1.

If you want to know more about using the 'Optimization' option I really recommend looking at NH7O's four-part tutorial at the address shown above. It says more than I ever could in the space available.

Using tapered tubing

This is a good opportunity to talk about modelling antennas that use tapered tubing. So far we have only looked at antennas with straight wires or straight tubing (don't forget that you have to specify the radius of the wire or tube on the **Geometry** tab. It usually defaults to a radius of 0.8mm if you don't change it).

But what if you are using tapered tubing? MMANA-GAL allows for that and even has an element editor option for you to make changes.

The way in which MMANA-GAL specifies that a wire in the Geometry table is to be tapered is by entering a negative integer in the R(mm) column. This negative radius is used as a pointer to a corresponding line in the 'Taper wire set' table (**Fig 4.6**) (which is found in the Edit menu).

Fig 4.6: You add your taper details in a table accessed from the edit menu

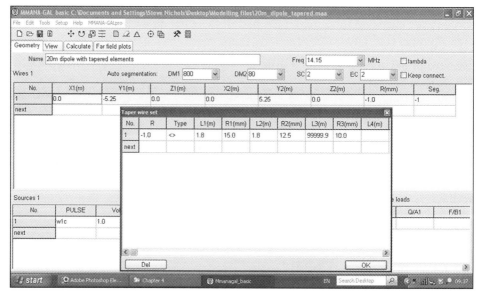

If all the wires in the antenna are tapered, then all the elements would have -1.0 as the radius. If there is another set of elements with a different taper, then they could have -2.0 as the radius. Many different taper sets can be used, but, usually only one set is needed.

In the 'Taper wire set' option you then have to include a line that is referenced by the negative radius you put in the Geometry table. That is, if you put '-1' in that table then you have to have a line that starts '-1' in the Taper wire set table.

You can specify if the taper is from the centre to both ends of the tubing by placing a '<>' symbol in the 'Type' box. You might use this is you have specified a single element (such as in a Yagi antenna) with the element stretching out from the zero X or Y coordinate to its ends.

If you have a single element and want to specify that the taper goes from one end to the other then you put a '>' symbol in, to show that the taper goes from the beginning of the wire to the end. Make sure you get this the right way round!

If building a vertical you use the same technique with the '>' symbol indicating that the taper goes from ground level to the tip – as long as you have specified that the start point of the vertical is at ground level.

The next columns are pairs of lengths in meters L(m), and radii in millimetres R(mm) that describe the actual tubing sizes used.

I have prepared a .maa file for you to see how this works – open up 20m_dipole_tapered.maa.

In this example, the centre section of tubing has a length of 1.8m, and a radius of 15mm. This section then telescopes onto the next smaller size tubing, with a length of 1.8m exposed, and a radius of 12.5mm. Note in this case that there will be two sections of this size, one on each end of the centre section.

The final sections, the end tips, have a radius of 10.0mm, but the length shown, '99999.9', is not to be taken literally. The width of the element is still defined by the Geometry table, and MMANA-GAL will automatically adjust the length of the outer sections of tubing so that the overall element length will equal this definition.

The '99999.9' label tells the program to use only enough of the end tubing to equal this length. In addition, while optimisation is in progress, only the end sections of the element are varied. The inner sections stay constant at the lengths defined in the table.

Don't forget that when using tapering it is the tube's radius you are interested in, not the diameter. That is, if you are using 10mm diameter tube the radius is 5mm.

I'm indebted to NH7O for this information as, once again, he has a very useful tutorial on tapering at *https://sites.google.com/a/wildblue.net/nh7o/mmana-gal-antenna-analysis/optimization-part4*

Using Loads

MMANA-GAL allows you to model loading coils and traps using the loads function. This becomes quite easy once you understand some of the basics.

To see where you specify loads go to the **Geometry** tab and look towards the bottom right of the screen. You will see a section marked 'Loads 0'.

Firstly, we use the same method we used to define the Source to show where we want to place the loading coil or trap. That is, we use the system of 'wire number/position'. So if we want to place a loading coil at the centre of wire one we would write 'w1c'. If we want it at the beginning of wire three we would write 'w3b'. This information goes in the box marked 'PULSE.'

Next to that is a box marked type, and this is asking us if the load is an inductor (L), a capacitor (C) or a trap (a combination of an inductor and a capacitor and noted by using the term 'LC').

In the next box (marked L/R/A0) we put the value of the inductor in microHenries (µH) and in the box to its right (marked C/jX/B0) we put the value of the capacitor in picoFarads (pF).

Obviously, if specifying a coil with the inductor symbol 'L' you specify the 'C' as zero. Likewise, if specifying a capacitor use the capacitor symbol 'C' and specify the 'L' as zero.

A trap has to have the designator 'LC' and a value in both the 'L' and 'C' fields.

The next box is the 'Q' value of the combination. If you don't know what it is put a typical value of 100.

MMANA-GAL is very clever in that if you are specifying a trap you only need to put in two values, say the value of 'L' and the frequency of operation (in the box marked 'F/B1') and it automatically works out the value of 'C' needed to make the trap resonant at that frequency.

You can also specify the loads as R+jX (complex), but that is beyond the scope of this introductory book, other than to say that you can define a terminating resistor, such as is used in a T2FD multiband antenna. You would do this by putting 'R+jX' in the 'Type' box and then specifying the resistance in the 'L/R/A0' box.

There is an example of this method being used in a T2FD tilted terminated folded dipole in MMANA-GAL's 'ANT>> Aperiodic' directory.

Back to how we actually use the Loads utility, let's pretend we want to make a shortened 80m dipole. Usually this would be about 42m long. For the sake of argument let's say we only had 20m to play with and want to put two inductors each at 6.4m from the feed point. So effectively we have two wires of 6.4m long, then the inductors, then two further wires of 3.35m, bringing the total length to 19.5m.

So what value inductor would we need to add in each leg to bring the antenna to resonance?

First, we design our antenna in MMANA-GAL (see my example provided in the sample files – '80m_loaded_dipole.maa'. In this I started off with values of the inductors of 100 µH. This gave a resonant frequency of 3.022MHz – obviously the inductors need to be smaller than 100 µH.

No.	PULSE	Type	L/R/A0	C/jX/B0	Q/A1	F/B1
1	w2e	LC	100	0	0.0	
2	w3e	LC	100	0	0.0	
next						

Loads 2 (L - uH; C - pF; R/jX - Ohm)　☑ Use loads

Fig 4.7: You can add loading coils or traps using the 'Loads' panel

So can MMANA-GAL actually work out what value they should be? Yes it can.

By going to the 'Optimization' button in the Calculate tab we can specify that we want to optimise the 'Loads' (**Fig 4.7**). Do this by first moving the sliders so that we are optimising for SWR (move that slider to the right and the others to the left).

Now click on the box on the first line where it says 'Type' and you will get a pop-up menu with a number of options on it. Select 'Load'. MMANA-GAL will automatically fill in the rest of the line and identify that you want to work with the load you have specified in position one.

Now do the same thing again on the next line, where it says 'Type', select 'load' and then edit it so that it reads 'Position 2'.

Now there is one small change we have to make, which is not so obvious.

If we just pressed 'Start' it would vary both the values of the inductors randomly to come up with the lowest SWR. In fact, if you do this you will find that it sets one inductor high and the other low with a very strange current distribution (although it finds a low-ish SWR). What we need to do is make sure that it alters both inductor values at the same time.

The way we do this is to form an 'association' between inductor one and inductor two. We do this by putting a '1' in the 'Associated' box for inductor number two in the 'Optimisation' window. This now means that whatever it does to inductor one it must do the same for inductor two.

Now we can press start. After running the optimisation routine you will see that it ends up selecting values of 64.5 µH for each inductor, giving a lowest possible SWR of 1.56:1 at 3.650MHz with the antenna at 20m height.

I have to admit I cheated a little. I found a design for a loaded 80m dipole on the internet and used the lengths of wires specified to put into MMANA-GAL.

The web site said you needed two inductors of 65 µH, so MMANA-GAL's calculation of 64.5 µH is pretty much spot on I think.

Fig 4.8:
MMANA-GAL
can even work
out how to build
the coils you
need

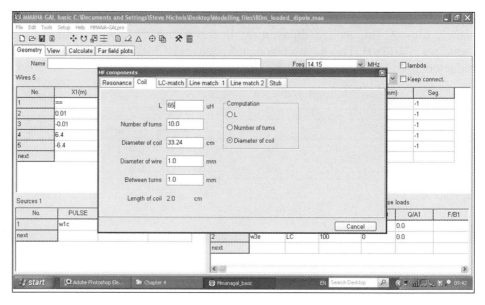

But it doesn't stop there. So how can you build an inductor of 65 μH? MMA-NA-GAL has the answer to that question too. From the top menu go to 'Tools>>HF components'. Now go to the 'Coil' tab (**Fig 4.8**). Put in the value of '65' into the box marked 'L', put in the diameter of the wire you wish to use and the diameter of the coil former and MMANA-GAL will tell you how many turns you need and even the length of the coil when you have finished.

Just another example of how MMANA-GAL is more powerful than you might think.

So to recap

You can build and model trapped verticals and dipoles using the 'LC' type in the loads section. Or you can design loading coils using the 'L' type. If your antenna is too long you can even calculate the value of 'C' that would be needed to bring it back to resonance for a given frequency too.

Using 'Lambda' measurements

In the examples I have given so far we have worked in metres – all of the measurements for the antennas have been metric. For me, this works best as I know what to cut and to what length.

However, MMANA-GAL also gives you the option of working in relative wavelength sizes. That is, with element lengths described in terms of fractions of lambda (λ).

To use this form of measurement just tick the box marked 'lambda' (**Fig 4.9**) in the **Geometry** tab. Now you can specify the coordinates in terms of fractions of a wavelength.

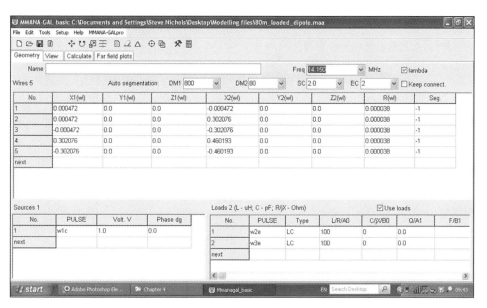

Fig 4.9:
Clicking the 'lambda' button converts all measurements into fractions of a wavelength

For example, setting the frequency in the Geometry tab to 14.050MHz and using the X1(wl) coordinate as 0.0 and the X2(wl) coordinate as 0.5 describes a half-wave dipole.

Running that as a calculation (to prove it works) gives an SWR of 2.15:1 and a resonant point of about 13.713MHz, proving that the antenna is a little too long. Reducing the antenna length to about 0.485 λ brings the resonant point to about 14.15MHz and gives a better match.

If using λ works for you then fine, but I prefer good old metres myself. One quick tip – if you go to the Calculate tab it will show you the wavelength in metres of your selected frequency (in MHz) in the main window.

Tools >>HF Components

I introduced you to the concept of the *HF Components* earlier when we talked about calculating how to build loading coils. Now let's take a look at all of the tools.

If you click on Tools >> HF components you will see that you end up with a pop-up window with a number of headings. Let's take each in turn.

Fig 4.10:
MMANA-GAL
will also work
out the reso-
nant frequency
of a coil/capaci-
tor combination

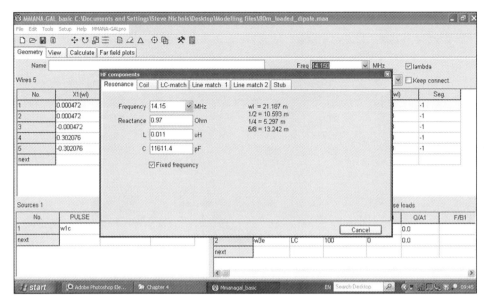

Resonance

The 'Resonance' tab (**Fig 4.10**) allows you to calculate the resonant frequency of an LC combination. You can pick a frequency, pick a value of inductance and it will calculate the required capacitance for you. Or you can pick the capacitance and it will calculate the inductance. It is also possible (by un-clicking the 'fixed frequency' option) to place values for inductance and capacitance and see what frequency you get. In terms of antennas this is invaluable when working out possible values for traps. It also calculates the reactance as well and includes a wavelength calculator, with automatically-calculated values for half, quarter and five-eighths wave radiators.

Coil

As outlined earlier, this allows you to calculate the diameter and number of turns required to create an inductor of a specific value. Alternatively, you can click on the 'Computation – L' option and work out what the inductance would be needed for a specific coil.

LC-Match

The 'LC match' tab displays a schematic diagram of an inductor and capacitor in parallel. You can decide whether the capacitance is in series or parallel and, again, the program will calculate the required values for a specific frequency.

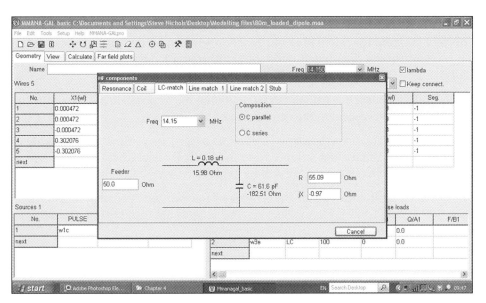

Fig 4.11: *It will even work out how to build matching circuits for you*

You can also select the impedance of the feeder. The tool can come in useful if trying to work out what matching network you might place at the feed point of a shortened antenna, perhaps vertical, to bring it to resonance. Artur SP2AGX shows how he used this approach to good effect to model a shortened vertical, and its associated matching network, for 80m on the web at:

http://sp2put.utp.edu.pl/index.php/2392,antena-pionowa-na-80m-druga-wers-ja?lang=en

In his model he used a 7m high vertical section with two 7m wires connected at the top, like a Marconi 'T'. Using MMANA-GAL this gave a predicted SWR of about 22:1 on 3.750MHz. Taking the calculated resistance (11.24 Ohms) and reactance (-99.22 Ohms) Artur was able to use the LC-match utility to calculate that to match the antenna to his 50 Ohm coax he would need a series inductance of 5.1 µH in parallel with a capacitance of 1576.6pF at the feed point to bring the antenna to resonance at 3.75MHz.

In fact, Artur didn't have to input anything as the program automatically transfers the resistance and reactance figures across to the 'LC-match' utility (**Fig 4.11**).

When the antenna was erected the figures were found to be 'ballpark', and he needed to change the values slightly to bring it to resonance where he wanted it. But overall, MMANA-GAL saved a lot of hassle and trial and error.

A copy of the antenna definition file for this design is available for you to play with – see: *80m_vertical_by_SP2AGX.maa*

Incidentally, This type of matching circuit is often used in automatic tuner (ATU) designs, where combinations of L and C are switched into circuit using microprocessor-controlled relays until the SWR is minimised.

Line match 1

This tool is useful for calculating impedance, Q-match section and a series-matching section using a distributed-constant circuit (eg a ladder feeder and a coaxial cable).

The overall impedance is calculated by obtaining the impedance of the output end of the feeder with respect to the impedance of the input end.

To use this, the antenna impedance can be measured by using a coaxial cable of arbitrary length and a noise bridge. Note the SWR is reduced if there is a loss in the transmission line – the theory will be explained in most antenna handbooks.

The Q-match section calculates the lengths of the two series-section transmission lines, when the TUNE button is clicked. The lengths are those that will result in a minimum SWR with respect to the input end (Ri).

MMANA-GAL assumes you are using no loss transmission line. The line length (L) is measured in wavelengths, and may require correction based on the velocity factor of the feeder to calculate the physical length. This is quite an advanced function.

Line match 2

This utility offers another way of calculating how to match loads (ZL) that are not 50 Ohms or resonant to your feeder. It shows how to use a combination of a shorted stub and an open-stub connected in parallel at the feed point to match to the input impedance (Zi). As the instructions say, it is useful to think of this arrangement as two section of transmission line, a capacitance (open-section) and an inductance (shorted section) of lines connected in parallel.

Stub

Finally, coaxial stubs are often used to match feeders to loads that are not 50 Ohms and purely resistive (that is, they exhibit reactance). A shorted stub is often used to provide a match, and behaves like a inductor. While an open-ended stub can also be used and will be found to behave like a capacitor. This utility gives you the option of choosing a shorted or open stub and then calculates the value as an inductance (coil) or a capacitance (capacitor). A coaxial stub can often be easier to make than a coil/capacitor combination.

Earth parameters/changing the constants

Out of the box, MMANA-GAL gives you the option of modelling your antennas in free space, over a perfect conductor and over real ground.

To be honest, it makes sense to do all your modelling over 'real' ground, for which MMANA-GAL presumes that you have a 'standard' earth, if there is such a thing, with a dielectric constant of 13 and a conductivity of 5 mS/m.

However, for the record, the average dielectric constants and conductivities for a range of different soil types are as follows:

Type of Ground	Dielectric constant	Conductivity (mS/m)
Sea water	81	4000
Fresh water	80	1 - 10
Wet ground	5 - 15	1 - 10
Dry field, forest	13	5
Sandy field	12	2
Suburb, industrial	5	1
Arid field	2 - 6	0.1

As you can see they vary wildly. One thing worth noting is the phenomenal dielectric constant and conductivity of sea water compared with ground, which explains why verticals mounted near to the sea's edge perform so well. In contrast, fresh water has a conductivity which is not much better than the standard 5 mS/m (millisiemens per metre) used by default in MMANA-GAL.

Modelling a vertical antenna (**Fig 4.12**) with the 81/4000 parameters for sea water compared with the standard 13/5 for dry field, for example, is quite an eye opener. You can easily gain up to 10 or more dB on low angle radiation from vertical antennas using sea water in your model.

By all means feel free to play with different values, but unless you really know what your soil type is like, and not just around the antenna but out to many wavelengths beyond, you might be better sticking with the defaults. And if you do change them, make sure you change them back!

MMANA-GAL also gives you the option of specifying ground radials in the 'Ground set-up' dialogue, saying how many and what radius of wire you are using. Interestingly, you can't say specify how long they are.

While you may not see a change in the calculated SWR by adding the ground radials (which is not necessarily what you would see in reality – if you don't have a perfect earth, adding radials usually lowers the feed point impedance as it starts to tend towards around 36 Ohms), don't be misled, it will result in better calculated far field results, especially on the low-angle radiation from ground-mounted verticals. Again, don't forget that it is a simulation – it is very easy to get hung up on predicted results.

Fig 4.12: Vertical antennas mounted next to the sea's edge can perform incredibly well

Conventional wisdom has it that ground-mounted verticals need up to 64-120 radials to work at maximum efficiency, although they don't necessarily have to be cut to a quarter wavelength as the earth detunes them. The general rule is 'more shorter' rather than 'fewer longer' radials is better for a given amount of wire.

One point, MMANA-GAL can't model buried radials. This was introduced into the NEC-4 software, which is able to perform Sommerfeld-Norton ground calculations. At this point you can shrug your shoulders and accept MMANA-GAL's limitations (after all it is free), or you can go buy a copy of EZNEC Pro/4, which is a NEC-4 based analysis program, for $650 and a NEC-4 non-US academic/ non-commercial licence for $500. It is up to you, free or $1,150.

Right-click options, including Search and Replace

MMANA-GAL is a very flexible program. If you open an antenna definition file, go to the Geometry tab, and right click you will see that you have a number of options.

One that is incredibly useful is the option to 'search and replace' (**Fig 4.13**). This can be a quick and easy way to replace dimensions. For example, say you have made a quad loop that has sides of 12m. But then you decide you want to model it with sides of 16m.

This is the kind of multi-band antenna that you might want to feed with open wire feeder (impedance 600 Ohms) or with a 4:1 balun (200 Ohms) and coax, so make sure you set the Standard Impedance (Z) to the appropriate value in the 'Set-up' menu before you start.

To change the geometry values manually could take some time, but with search and replace you can do it in seconds – changing the 'X' and 'Y' values from '6' and '-6' to '8' and '-8'.

*Fig 4.13:
The search and replace function can save a lot of hard work when resizing antenna designs*

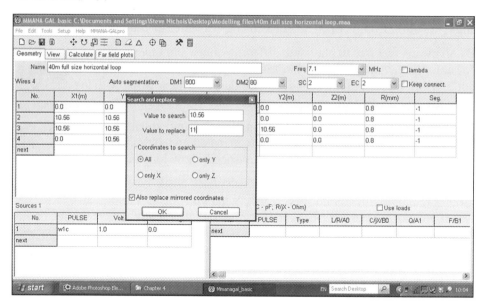

As, in this case we started by giving the first wire values of '-6' and '6' so that it was symmetrical about the X and Y axis, MMANA-GAL can even work out that you want to change both of them. All you have to do is tick the 'Also replace mirrored coordinates' option.

The program will also let you select whether you want to replace all the coordinates with those values, or just those on the X, Y or Z axes.

If you want to play with this yourself, I have set up a file for you to try – just use 'Search_and_replace.maa', which is the antenna definition file for the 12m per side quad.

Incidentally, the model showed that a quad of side length 16m had a reasonably low SWR on 20m and 10m when mounted at 10m and fed with a 4:1 balun. It also had some high gain lobes on 10m (28MHz). Fed with open wire feeder a quad loop can make a very good multiband antenna! Try playing with the model and see for yourself.

MMANA-GAL also gives you the right-click option of replacing the start and end point of a wire. That is, effectively turning the wire upside down in terms of its coordinates. You can also move coordinates up and down the X, Y or Z axes using the 'Move' command.

Segmentation and Tapering

I have deliberately left this section as long as I can as it is quite complex and potentially confusing.

MMANA-GAL works by breaking up your antenna design into parts or segments, calculating the current flow in each segment, solving Maxwell's equations for each segment at the frequency you have chosen and then summing all of these individual electromagnetic fields together to give the overall result and far field patterns.

The authors (and the originators of NEC) deserve a medal for getting it to be able to do that alone!

But the actual number of segments used and the method of segmentation strongly influences the calculation's accuracy. This is particularly true when an element is bent (eg a circular loop antenna). In this case the element has to be segmented into smaller pieces, but only around the bending point of the element. This is achieved by using fine tapering.

Tapering is one of the methods that improves the calculation accuracy. It divides the element section near the bending point into smaller segments, but divides the other sections (straight sections) into larger segments. If all the elements were divided into small segments, the computation time would increase considerably. Tapering using a small number of segments on a straight element will produce accurate results. Too few segments, and the model's accuracy will be poor, too many and the computation time gets longer.

MMANA-GAL defaults to an automatic method of tapering that increases the amount of segmentation where it thinks it is needed. That is, the segments are smallest near any discontinuity, such as telescoped tubing, at a sharp turn, or at element end.

If you look at the **Geometry** tab you will see that 'Seg' is set to '-1'. As a beginner it is best to leave this as it is, along with the default 'Auto segmentation' values.

If you are designing antennas that have wires very close together, or many bends you may need to increase the amount of segmentation to get accurate results. But if you don't know what you are doing you can seriously screw up the program's accuracy.

If you want to read more about segmentation there is a section in the MMA-NA-GAL help files that outlines what it is and how it works. The MMANA-GAL user group on Yahoo also has a number of experts who can help if you get stuck with a design.

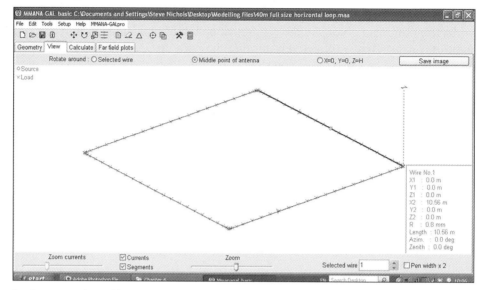

In the meantime, if you want to see how MMANA-GAL has broken your antenna design up into segments, just select the 'Segments' box (**Fig 4.14**) when you are looking at the View tab and it will show you.

Using 'Keep connected'

On the **Geometry** tab you will see there is a box (under lambda) marked 'Keep connect.' When checked, this ensures that the dimensions of all the elements connected to the target element can be re-scaled, without losing the connection to the target element. Otherwise, it would be very difficult to design a Yagi or loop antenna if all of the elements' X-Y-Z coordinates had to be changed every time.

You can try this with the antenna definition file we played with earlier – Search_ and_replace.maa. Open the file, go to the 'Wire edit' view on the Calculate tab and select the 'XY' view. Now if you click and drag one of the points you will see that the other wires move too, just as if they are all connected. This is a quick and easy way to resize loop antennas.

Saving far fields and comparing results

MMANA-GAL can not only calculate far field results for any given design, but it can also compare them from two or more different antennas.

To do this, first create your antenna design, calculate the results and then go to **Far field plots**. At this point you can save this plot by going to 'File >> Save far fields'. The file will be saved with the extension .mab. However, before you do that a word of advice. MMANA-GAL automatically shows the Azimuth (left hand) plot for the best angle of radiation or sometimes 45 degrees. Clicking on the 'Elevation' button will show you what this angle is. If you are comparing plots, they will only make sense if you are comparing like with like. That is, both plots should preferably be at the same elevation angle.

So, before you save the plot make sure you have selected the elevation angle you with to compare, by going to 'Elevation' and typing in the angle you wish and pressing 'OK'. Now you can save the far field plot. I usually add the elevation angle to my file name to remind me, eg 10m_dipole_10degrees.mab or something similar.

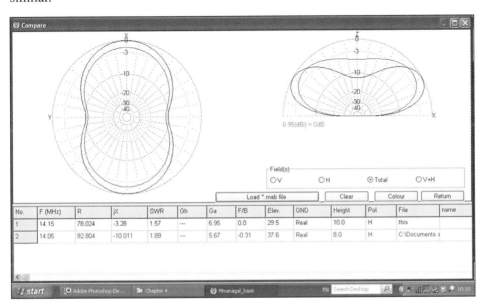

Fig 4.15: MMANA-GAL lets you compare the far field patterns of different antennas or configurations

Now, that you have saved the plot you can open up the next antenna, run the simulation and go to the **Far field plots** tab (**Fig 4.15**). Again, make sure you now select the elevation angle you wish to check. Now, if you go to 'Tools >>Compare' and then select 'Load *.mab file' you will be able to select the previous far field plot you saved and MMANA-GAL will automatically display both of them together.

Note that you can select the vertically-polarised portion of the field, the horizontal, or the combined field.

Incidentally, you may have noticed that there is no way of saving the screens that you see. I always save mine by hitting the 'Print Screen' button on my keyboard and then pasting them into a new file on my image editing program. Once I have done that I can save them as .JPG images.

I use Adobe Photoshop Elements, which was the method used to save all the images you see in this book, but it also seems to work with the Paint program that comes with Windows. Try saving some screen grabs with whatever program you use for image editing.

Saving data to a .csv file and creating a graph

If you are really keen on using MMANA-GAL sooner or later you might want to be able to graph your results.

At first glance there isn't an easy way to do this, but bear with me!

MMANA-GAL gives you the option of saving your raw data as a comma-delimited file (.csv). The program can save data from the frequency, current, near field, elevation angle, gain, SWR and impedance results (**Fig 16**).

It can also automatically calculate the resistance and reactance results for a whole band using the 'File>>Create list F/R/jX *nwl' option. Personally, I am more interested in the SWR results so the example I will give will focus on that.

Let's say, for example, that you have modelled an off-centre fed dipole and want a plot of the SWR from 3.5-30MHz.

First, create your design, test it to make sure it works the way it should and that you are getting the far field plots you expect.

Now, go to 'File >> Table F/SWR/Gain/Z *.csv' option.

On this screen you can select the range that you wish to test. So put '3.5' into the Fmin box and '30' into the Fmax box. Then select a suitable step for the test, say 50kHz. MMANA-GAL will automatically work out the number of steps, and therefore data points, that will be produced.

For example, scanning an antenna design from 3-30MHz in 50kHz steps will result in 541 data points. That's reasonable and won't overtax the program too much.

Fig 4.16: Importing the output CSV file from MMANA-GAL into Excel lets you create graphs of SWR over a wide frequency range

Make sure you have selected the 'not match' box as we want to see all the results, not just the good ones! Now press 'OK' and give it a suitable filename. At this stage it will look like nothing is happening, but it is. MMANA-GAL is busily working away in the background to perform the calculations and you won't be able to close the window or cancel it until it has finished.

Note that this can take many minutes before it has finished, especially if you have selected a wide frequency range and a small step or have a less powerful computer.

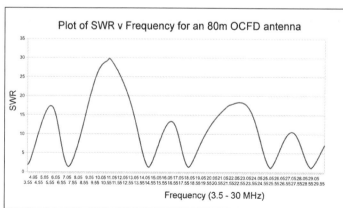

Plot of SWR v Frequency for an 80m OCFD antenna

Frequency (3.5 - 30 MHz)

Once it has finished you will regain control of the program and be able to open the .csv (comma delimited) file that you have created. If in doubt, clicking on the .csv file will result in a 'File in Use' warning if it hasn't finished the run.

Once you have this file you can open it in Excel or a similar spreadsheet program, and select the options you wish to graph, such as frequency v SWR. An open source spreadsheet program like OpenOffice Calc will also work and is free – we've included the OpenOffice suite on the CD-ROM.

I can't tell you exactly how you can import the CSV data into your spreadsheet as it will vary from program to program, but any good book will explain it for you, or you can use trial and error (I get good results with Excel and OpenOffice Calc). Usually, the most important thing is to make sure you have selected 'comma delimited' as the data type when opening the file. Then you just have to make sure you only select the columns you wish to graph, such as frequency v SWR (usually selecting the columns you want while holding down the 'CTRL' button).

Hint: if using OpenOffice Calc, once you have selected the 'Freq(MHz)' and 'SWR (50.0 Ohm)' columns, select the graphing icon and then the 'Line' graph option.

On the next screen select 'Data series in columns' and tick 'First row as label' and 'First column as label'. This will give you the graph you want.

I have found this method invaluable when looking at the characteristics of multi-band antennas as you can see where the antenna works well and where it doesn't.

Final comments

As this is an introductory guide to antenna modelling I feel that we have barely scratched the surface of what MMANA-GAL can do and all its functionality.

If you wish to explore some of the other options in the program I suggest joining the user group at Yahoo or Googling MMANA-GAL to see what is out there. As I said earlier, there are also a lot of excellent YouTube videos (**Fig 4.17**) that will show, rather than tell, you what the program will do and how to do it.

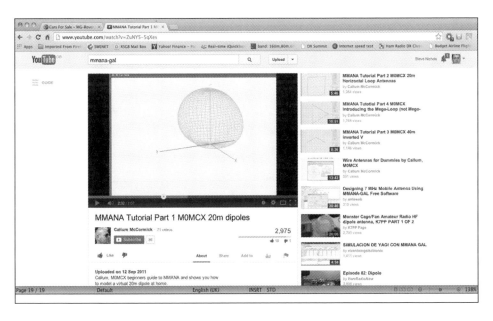

Fig 4.17: There are lots of MMANA-GAL tutorials to watch on YouTube

Meanwhile, the next chapter is devoted to showing you how MMANA-GAL can be used in real-life.

The examples will show you how radiation patterns can vary with an antenna's height; how so-called multi-band antenna designs are often anything but; and how moving the feed point of an off-centre fed dipole can make it work on more bands.

We'll also look at how vertical antennas can produce very low-angle radiation and how turning a dipole into an inverted V can ruin an antenna's DX performance.

Worked Examples of MMANA-GAL

Dipoles – how height can affect DX performance

In this example, we are going to take one of the antenna definition files that comes with MMANA-GAL and see what effect height above ground has on the antenna's radiation pattern. It is actually an antenna we saw earlier, but this time we will look at it in more detail.

So go ahead, start MMANA-GAL and navigate to the 'ANT >> HF Simple >> Dipole >> DP20.MAA file'.

This is about as simple as its gets – a half wave wire dipole for 20m (14MHz) consisting of a single element of radius 1mm that is 10.35m long (running from x = -5.17m to x = +5.17m. It is also fed in the centre (with the source = w1c).

Now go to the **Calculate** tab and make sure that you have selected 'real' for the ground and the material as copper (Cu) wire. Set the frequency as 14.150MHz which is close to mid band and the height as 5m.

Now press 'Start'. You'll quickly see that the SWR (at 50 Ohms) is 2.25:1. Going to 'Plots >> SWR' and then pressing 'Resonance' shows us that the resonant point is actually about 13.7MHz.

If we then go to the 'Far fields' tab in that window you can see that this is very much a cloud warmer – most of the radiation goes straight up because of the antenna's low height. This isn't what we want for a 20m antenna.

OK, let's give the antenna some height. Go back to the **Calculate** tab and change the 'Add height' to 10m and run again.

Now the SWR has come down to 1.56:1 (**Fig 5.1**) and if you check, the resonant point has risen to 14.300MHz. Looking at the 'Far fields' tab you will see that the angle of maximum radiation has come down to around 30 degrees and that the dipole is showing signs of directivity off its sides.

OK, let's go and change the height to 15m and run again. Now the SWR has changed to 1.64:1, the resonant point has gone down to 13.96MHz and the far field plot shows the maximum angle of radiation is now about 18 degrees, but a vertical lobe has broken out.

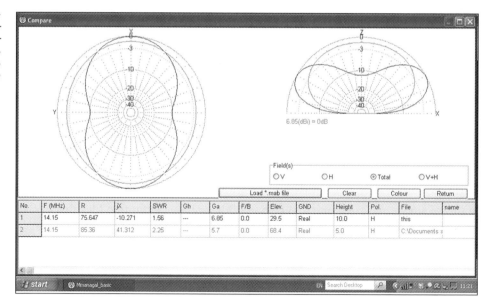

No.	F (MHz)	R	jX	SWR	Gh	Ga	F/B	Elev.	GND	Height	Pol.	File	name
1	14.15	75.647	-10.271	1.56	---	6.85	0.0	29.5	Real	10.0	H	this	
2	14.15	85.36	41.312	2.25	---	5.7	0.0	68.4	Real	5.0	H	C:\Documents a	

At 20m height the SWR changes yet again to 1.59:1, the resonant point moves back to 14.15MHz and that vertical lobe has broken into two high-angle lobes, although the maximum angle of radiation is now down to 14 degrees.

You can play this game all day, but we find a number of interesting points:

The actual SWR or feed point impedance of an antenna (in this case a dipole) can vary quite dramatically with height. This is why it is best to model your antennas at the height you will actually mount them, otherwise their length could be way off.

For maximum radiation at the lowest angles, generally the higher the antenna is the better. Note that this doesn't necessarily mean higher is better for all contacts. On close in or intermediate distance contacts there could be a big advantage in having a higher-angle radiation lobe.

A dipole is directional, perpendicular to its centre and this can mean that you need to be able to rotate it – this directionality can get more acute the higher you mount the antenna.

If you want to play further, try changing the earth parameters to those of sea water – dielectric constant 81, conductivity 4000 mS/m. Running the calculations again with the antenna at 10m high shows that the radiation angle is not that much different to having the horizontal antenna over normal earth at a typical height of 10m. This shows that verticals are the way to go on the beach!

Inverted Vs – how does the 'V' angle affect radiation?

Inverted V antennas have a good following, probably because they only need a single central support. But what do you gain by having your antenna as an inverted V and what do you lose?

Let's use the inverted V model for 20m that I have created for you. The file is called 'Sample 20m Inverted v.maa' and consists of two wires of length 5.16m with their apex at 10m, sloping down so that their ends are at 8m.

If we now run this at 14.15MHz we see an SWR of 1.5:1 and a resonant point of about 14.19MHz. If we go to far field plots we can see that the radiation pattern is very similar to that produced by the flat-top 20m dipole we had before with the maximum radiation perpendicular to the antenna and at about 30 degrees. You might like to save the far field plot using the 'File >> Save far fields' command, making sure that the 'Elevation' is set to 30 degrees before you do.

In this configuration the included angle between the two legs is about 135 degrees and all seems to be working well. But conventional wisdom has it that the included angle on an inverted V should not be less than about 120 degrees. So let's see how that works out in the model.

Now open up the file 'Sample 20m Inverted vB.maa'. I have saved you the trouble of creating the antenna yourself, but the apex is still at 10m, but the legs come down at 45 degrees, giving an included angle of 90 degrees (**Fig 5.2**). This could be similar to what you might have to do in a small garden plot, but let's see what it does to the performance.

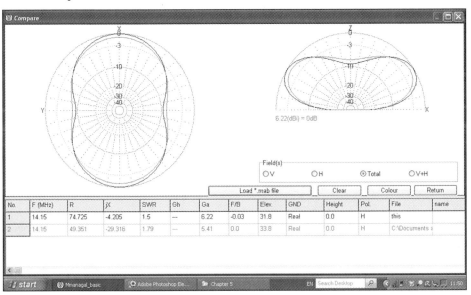

Fig 5.2: *The difference between an inverted V with an included angle of 90 degrees and another of 135 degrees appears minimal at an apex height of 10m*

No.	F (MHz)	R	jX	SWR	Gh	Ga	F/B	Elev.	GND	Height	Pol.	File	name
1	14.15	74.725	-4.205	1.5	---	6.22	-0.03	31.8	Real	0.0	H	this	
2	14.15	49.351	-29.316	1.79	---	5.41	0.0	33.8	Real	0.0	H	C:\Documents	

Run the program, go to 'Plots' and do a 'compare' with the far field plot you did for the first inverted V dipole. What you see is the dipole with the included angle of about 90 degrees is very similar to the inverted V with the included angle of 135 degrees.

However, play with the heights and you see that even putting the centre of the inverted V up another two metres (to 10m) (**Fig 5.3**) increases the low-angle gain by up to around 3dB.

You can play with other variants, but what you discover is that the inverted V is not a bad performer, as long as you keep the centre as high as possible and try to keep the included angle as broad as you can. Yes, the performance is not quite as good as a flat top, but for a single-band antenna, operating on its normal frequency, say 20m, it isn't too much of a compromise. Later, I'll show that longer multiband antennas fair worse when pushed into service as an inverted V on the higher bands.

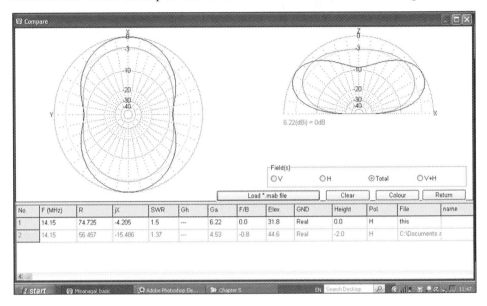

Fig 5.3:
But lowering the height of the apex of the either inverted V makes a big difference to the low-angle radiation

The G5RV multiband dipole

The G5RV antenna has long been a favourite of radio amateurs.

For those not familiar with the antenna it was designed by Louis Varney G5RV and consists of a 102ft (31.1m) dipole top with a 28.5ft (8.5m) centre section made out of open wire feeder or 300 Ohm windowed ribbon cable. You then connect your 50 Ohm coax to the bottom. I say 28.5ft, but in reality this depends on the velocity factor (VF) of the ribbon cable.

Some designs say 34.5ft (10.36m) for the matching section others say that ribbon cable with 'windows' has a velocity factor that will almost be that of open-wire feeder so its mechanical length should be 30.6ft (9.3m).

The actual length is supposed to an electrical half wavelength at 20m, so the reality is that you should really cut this accurately or calculate the VF of the cable you intend to use and act accordingly. A trick is that a half wavelength of a cable will reflect the impedance of its far end. I have soldered a 50 Ohm resistor across the end of a length of 300 Ohm ribbon and cut it until I have seen a 1:1 SWR at the far end (with the analyser set to 50 Ohms) at the frequency I wanted. Bingo, you then know it is a half wavelength long.

MMANA-GAL comes with an antenna definition file for the G5RV. Go to 'ANT >>HF multibands >>Ant+Tuner >> G5RV.maa' and open it up **(Fig 5.4)**.

This uses two wires of radius 1.5mm at a distance of 2cm as the matching section, and two legs of 15.54 m, giving a total span of 31.08m (102 feet). The file has the antenna top at 13.2m and the feed point (source) at 0.1m.

So let's go play. Firstly, run the program with zero additional height, real ground and copper (Cu) wire. Out of the box, the MMANA-GAL file is set up to run with 75 Ohm cable at the feed point. I suggest you change this to 50 Ohms using the 'Set-up' menu.

What you will find is that the model predicts that the antenna will only offer a fair SWR (below 3:1) on 40m (SWR 1.9:1) and 10m (SWR 1.3:1). On some bands it is reasonable, but outside of the range of many internal ATUs – one highly-regarded range of transceivers can't match anything above about 3:1.

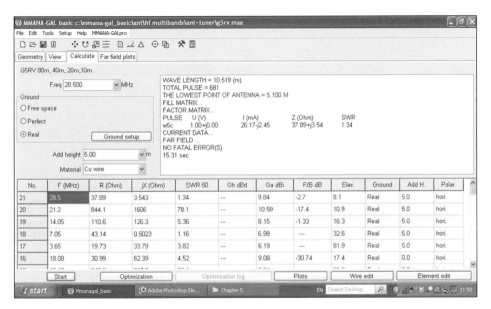

Fig 5.4:
The G5RV only offers a reasonable match on a few bands

For example, on 80m the best SWR is about 5:1 at 3.5MHz, 20m (best SWR about 6:1, and 17m (about 5:1). On other bands the SWR is rotten – 30m (SWR 75:1), 15m (SWR 61:1) and 12m (SWR 21:1).

So as a multiband antenna the G5RV fails pretty miserably due to line losses for any reasonable length of coax, and the poor ability of some ATUs to match these loads.

If you now look at the far field plots for the G5RV (**Fig 5.5**) you will see that it is 'lobey' indeed on the higher bands. Whether you consider this a good antenna or not will depend entirely on whether the station you want to work is on a lobe or in a null. For the lower bands, say 80m and 40m, the plots are not much different to those of a full-size dipole.

Fig 5.5:
*Mounted as
a flat top, the
G5RV offers a
complex radia-
tion pattern on
the higher fre-
quencies with
many lobes –
this is 10m*

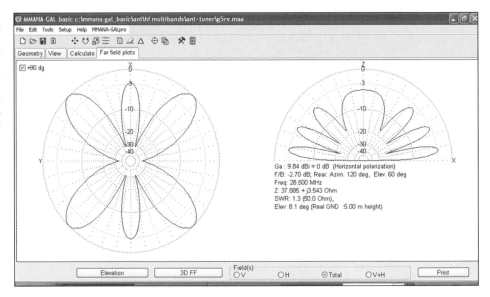

If you want to take this further, using the 'wire edit' menu you can turn the G5RV into an inverted V (**Fig 5.6**) – keeping each leg about 15.54m long and with the apex at the original height. I have saved a version of this called 'G5RV inverted V.maa' if you don't wish to make the model yourself.

Now run the program again and you will see that the radiation patterns, although now more omnidirectional, have lost a lot of gain in their lobes at the higher frequencies (20m and above) and its low angle performance has deteriorated badly.

Fig 5.6:
*As an inverted
V on 20m it
becomes more
omnidirectional,
but you lose a
lot of gain*

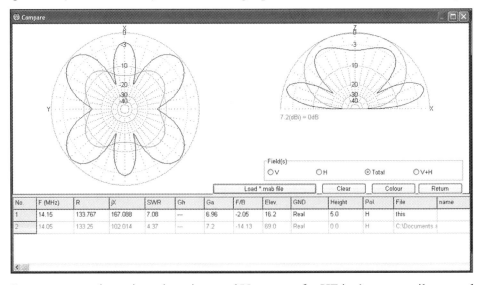

So you can see that using a long inverted V antenna for HF isn't necessarily a good idea. You are probably better off with two antennas – one for the low bands (80m and 40m) and another for the higher ones (30-10m).

If you want to play with the model for a G5RV a little more, I found that two wires of radius 1.5mm and spaced 0.02m (+0.01m and -0.01m) apart approximated to an impedance of 300 Ohm fairly well. I checked this by modelling a 300 Ohm resistor across the end (in MMANA-GAL) and measuring the impedance with a 300 Ohm source.

By varying the length of the feeder and the two wires attached you can make the 'G5RV' provide a better match on some bands. Brian ZS6BKW did just this, using a 28.53m 'top' and around 11.1m of 300 Ohm ribbon. I have supplied a tentative model of the ZS6BKW for you to play with, called 'Optimised G5RV – ZS6BKW. maa' – I say 'tentative' as we don't know the exact velocity ratio of the ribbon cable used. I ended up with 13.85m of 'feeder', which would probably equate to about 12.6m in real life allowing for the velocity ratio of the cable.

The match is better on some bands, notably 40, 20, 12 and 10m, but it still doesn't match on 30m and 15m.

If I were building one of these for real I would use a flat top of 28.52m and then adjust the length of the 300 Ohm ribbon cable to get the lowest SWR in the middle of the 20m band, cutting it too long to start with.

But why not play with the lengths in MMANA-GAL and see what you can do?

The W3DZZ trapped dipole

As MMANA-GAL allows us to place combinations of L (inductance) and C (capacitance) into the design we can play with trap dipoles, including the famous W3DZZ.

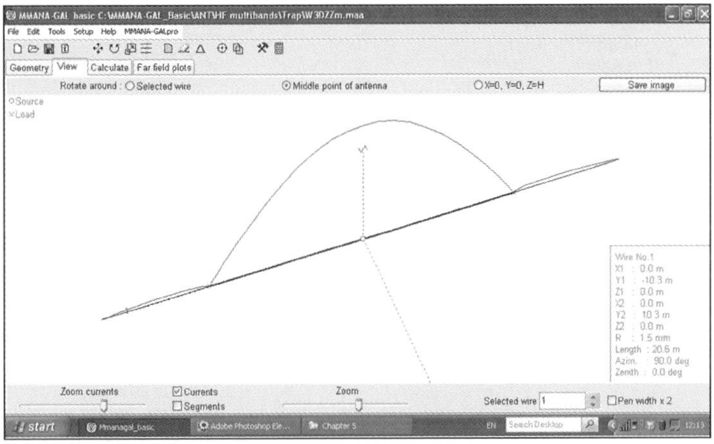

Fig 5.7: Traps effectively block the antenna current as you can see in this example of a W3DZZ trap dipole working on 40m

This is often touted as being a multi-band antenna, but is it? The W3DZZ consists of a 108ft (32.92m) flat top dipole with two 40m traps fitted. The inductance of the traps means it offers a low SWR on 80m, and the traps mean that it also resonates on 40m. But what about the other bands?

MMANA-GAL comes with an antenna definition file for the W3DZZ. It can be found at 'ANT\HF multibands\Trap\ W3DZZ.maa' (**Fig 5.7**).

Running this design with the top at 10m shows that the lowest SWR point on 80m is 3.55MHz at about 1.85:1. On 40m it comes in at about 1.7:1 at 7MHz. So far so good.

But the antenna was designed before the WARC bands were introduced so 10MHz/30m (SWR 54:1), 18MHz/17m (SWR 75:1) and 24MHz/12m (SWR 58.3:1) appear to be no-go areas.

Even 14MHz/20m is above 6:1 and 28MHz/10m is 36:1, although 21MHz/15m is a more respectable 2.5:1.

One thing you can try is to play with the values of the L and C in the traps to see if you can find a combination that gives lower SWR values. I have never found one that covers all the bands, although an internet search for 'W3DZZ' will find all sorts of combinations, where some do better than others.

So again, MMANA-GAL shows that the original W3DZZ isn't truly a multi-band antenna, at least when fed with coax, but you haven't had to build a thing to find out!

Fig 5.8:
MMANA-GAL will let you model traps, although you will still need to use another calculator if building coax versions like this one

Vertical/Ground Plane antennas

The program is also very good at modelling vertical antennas (**Fig 5.8**). In fact, I used it to model my own end-fed half wave (EFHW) design and the subsequent multi-band version with two traps.

MMANA-GAL comes with quite a few samples to get you going, so let's start with the file 'ANT\HF Simple\Vertical\GP40.maa'. This is a simple quarter wave vertical for 40m that is 10.6m high and fed against four radials, again each of 10.6m. You will find that if you try and run this with zero height added you will get the error 'The lowest point of the antenna=0.000m'. This is because the radials are effectively sitting on the ground. If you are trying to model a ground-mounted vertical just add height of about 0.1m. This will make the program work properly.

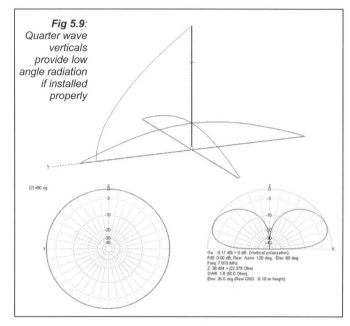

Fig 5.9:
Quarter wave verticals provide low angle radiation if installed properly

Running a calculation in this configuration shows a low SWR of about 1.45:1 at 6.835MHz. In other word, the antenna is too long and needs to be cut back to about 10.2m to bring the resonant point to about 7.1MHz.

However, if we raise the base of the antenna to a height of about 5m the resonant point is fine at about 7.1MHz with the original length. This again goes to show that height above ground can affect impedance.

The far field plots show that the antenna is a good DX performer with a low angle maximum of about 26 degrees (-0.2 dBi) when ground mounted and about 19 degrees (also -0.2 dBi) when mounted at 5m high.

Note that this is around an S point worse than a half-wave dipole at the same elevation angle, probably because of the imperfect earth. Adding 16 radials (in the 'ground setup' option) (**Fig 5.10**) increases the gain for the ground-mounted version to about 1.1dBi. As in real life, the more radials you can get down the better.

As an experiment, try running MMANA-GAL with 21.050MHz selected as the frequency. You will see that the 40m quarter wave vertical also offers a low SWR on 15m, due to it being three quarters of a wavelength long. But take a look at the far field plots and you will see that you have now lost that low-angle radiation, which is replaced with a high angle maximum at about 43 degrees.

So while a quarter-wave vertical for 40m could be pressed into service on 15m it is unlikely to set the world on fire in terms of DX.

*Fig 5.10:
The secret to an effective vertical is adding plenty of radials*

The Rybakov 7.6m vertical

The Rybakov antenna is so called because it means means 'fisherman' or 'family of the fisherman' in Russian and uses a fibreglass fishing pole. It is a popular and cheap antenna that can be pressed into service as a multi-band.

Designed by Enrico (IV3SBE) and Mauro (IV3SCP) it is essentially a 7.6m vertical fed with a 4:1 unun (unbalanced to unbalanced transformer) and an earth stake/radials – the more the merrier.

It works very well with a fibreglass fishing pole and can be put up in a few minutes.

The idea is that the antenna represents a non 50 Ohm (1:1 SWR) match at all frequencies – 7.6m is chosen as it isn't actually a half wave (high impedance) or quarter wave (low impedance) on any band. In other words it is designed to be NON-resonant on any of the amateur bands.

The unun transforms the impedance to something closer to 1:1 and therefore reduces coax losses. But it still needs an ATU to match it.

But what does MMANA-GAL make of it? I created a file for you to try. It is called 'rybakov.maa' (**Fig 5.11**), but make sure the impedance or standard Z is set to 200 Ohms before you start (see the 'Setup' menu). You will notice that 200 is not an option in the drop down menu. Don't worry – just type in '200' and press enter and it will be fine and mimic a 4:1 un-un.

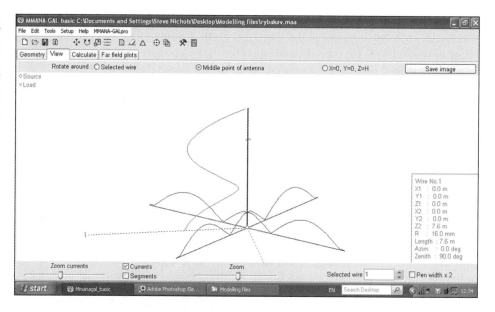

Fig 5.11:
*The Rybakov
will work from
40-10m, but the
patterns are
less than ideal
on 10m due to
it being a little
too long*

Running MMANA-GAL at 14.150MHz shows an SWR of 3.8:1. By the time you factor in some coax loss this should be within the range of most internal ATUs. On 17m (18MHz) it is about 5.1:1, on 21, 24 and 28MHz it is less than about 7:1. It will even work on 30m (10MHz) where it is about 4.5:1, although 40m (7MHz) is a bit of a stretch and you might struggle to get it to match.

Measurements at the feed point of my own real-life Rybakov showed that the actual SWR was below 6:1 everywhere.

The radiation pattern on 10MHz, 14MHz and 18MHz is typical of a vertical and good for DX. It is not so good on the higher bands as the antenna gets progressive longer than a quarter wave and the pattern gets complex.

If you want one to work predominantly on 40m and 30m you can try extending the vertical length to 8.6m – try modelling that in MMANA-GAL and see what happens to the SWR on those bands.

As a cheap and cheerful multi-band vertical the Rybakov works reasonably well, as long as you give it a decent set of radials and have an ATU for the mismatch.

End-fed Half-Wave HF Vertical

This was another antenna that featured in my book 'Stealth Antennas'. It consists of a half-wave vertical radiator fed with a special matching unit to match the 2000-3000 or so Ohms impedance to the 50 Ohm feeder. I won't go into the construction details here, but you don't necessarily have to buy my book (although I would like you to!). Just Google 'EFHW' and you should be able to find them.

But what I wanted to show was how well the antenna works for DX and how MMANA-GAL can show you why. Open up the file EFHW.maa and ensure that the impedance or standard Z is set to 2000 Ohms before you start (see the 'Setup' menu).

Now run the program with a frequency of 14.150MHz (**Fig 5.12**) and you will see that it predicts an SWR lower than 2:1. The actual impedance at the end of a half wave can vary and the real antenna will be better than this.

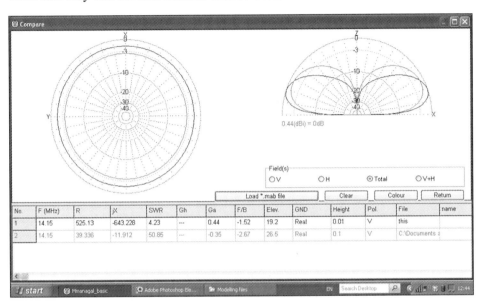

Fig 5.12:
The end fed half-wave (if matched properly) offers a lower angle of radiation than a quarter-wave ground plane

No.	F (MHz)	R	jX	SWR	Gh	Ga	F/B	Elev.	GND	Height	Pol.	File	name
1	14.15	525.13	-643.228	4.23	---	0.44	-1.52	19.2	Real	0.01	V	this	
2	14.15	39.336	-11.912	50.85	---	-0.35	-2.67	26.5	Real	0.1	V	C:\Documents a	

Now go to the far field plots and you will see that the antenna is a very good low-angle performer even when ground mounted.

As a mono-band antenna it works very well. I have even made a trapped version (with traps for 15m and 17m) that works well with a single matching box. The file for this is called efhw_multiband_20_17-15.maa.

The 43ft vertical

Many US manufacturers advertise 43ft verticals. But what is magical about 43ft? At first glance it doesn't appear to be a quarter wavelength at any particular amateur frequency, which actually gives us a big clue.

The 43ft vertical is designed to be non-resonant at any ham frequency and is meant to be fed with a 4:1 un-un. Luckily, with MMANA-GAL we can model its performance and see what you are likely to get in real-life.

So go ahead and open up the file '43ft_vertical.maa'.

Looking at a US manufacturer's web site they claim that the antenna can be used from 160m to 10m. Presuming that they mean you need to use a 4:1 unun to achieve this let's start by setting the feed impedance to 200 Ohms (Set up >> Standard Z = 200 Ohm).

In the model I have specified tapered aluminium tubing and a 32 wire ground radials.

Running the calculation on 1.825MHz (top band) shows an SWR of around 972:1 at 200 ohms. If you were to feed this antenna at the base with a 4:1 un-un and then 20m of RG-213 you would effectively have line losses of about 13dB according to the coax loss calculator at *http://www.saarsham.net/coax.html*. So you put 100W in and get about 5W at the feed point, less any un-un losses.

Hmm. That doesn't sound very good to me, assuming your tuner could match that kind of mismatch at the rig end. If you have to use a 43ft vertical on top band I think your best bet would be to install a remote tuner at the base of the antenna – at least it would cut the line losses.

Looking at the far field plots, the gain at 10 degrees elevation would be about 2.6 dBi, so as long as you can sort out the matching issues it would work OK for DX on top band.

But what about 3.5MHz? At 3.650MHz the SWR comes out at a more respectable (?) 40.6:1. Here, line losses with 20m of RG213 would be about 3.3 dB which is better, although you would still be better matching it at the base of the antenna and not in the shack. Again, the radiation pattern would be good for DX.

On 40m the antenna starts to shine – the SWR is about 4:1 at the feed point with the 4:1 un-un, the far field plot is still good and all is well. Likewise, 30m (10MHz) where the SWR is 6.39:1 and could be matched fairly easily at the end of the coax if need be.

Fig 5.13:
With the 43ft
vertical the
pattern starts to
go 'high angle'
on 20m and
above

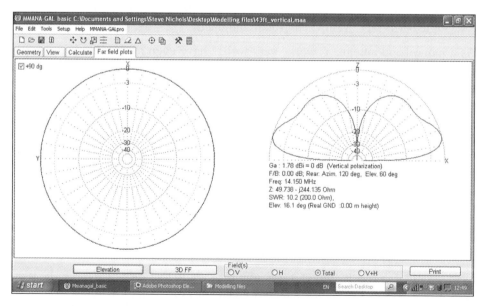

Moving up to 20m (SWR 10.2:1) and the radiation pattern starts to break into both a high lobe and a low lobe, which gives you the best of both worlds if you want both near and distant contacts. But from 17m and upwards the patterns start to go increasingly 'high angle', even though the SWR figures are reasonable.

By the time you get to 10m the maximum radiation angle is about 55 degrees and I think you would find it disappointing for all but sporadic E contacts in the summer.

So, in conclusion, MMANA-GAL tells us that the antenna is really at its best on 40m-20m (**Fig 5.13**), but can be made to work on top band (160m) and 80m with some effort, plus will work-ish at higher frequencies. At least you can now make that $200 purchase with a little more knowledge of how it is likely to perform, thanks to the completely free MMANA-GAL program.

The Off Centre Fed Dipole (OCFD)

Technically, what I am about to describe is an off-centre fed dipole, but you some-times hear these described as Windoms, although the original Windom had a single line feed to the main antenna wire.

The Windom was first designed in 1923 by William Litell Everitt, but Loren G Windom, W8GZ, wrote about it in the September 1929 issue of QST Magazine and the name stuck.

In the form I am about to describe the OCFD is a dipole with one leg 27.74m (91ft) long and the other 13.72m (45ft) long to give a total length of 41.46m (136ft). It is fed at the junction of the two wires with a 4:1 balun and the coax feed falls away vertically from the antenna.

We briefly looked at this earlier with a snapshot of an SWR sweep from 3-30MHz.

To save you the effort of modelling this I have created the file for you – see 'OCF-D_80m.maa'. The antenna is set to zero height, so that you can adjust it with the 'Add height' command. Starting off at a height of 20m you find that the antenna has a low SWR of less than 2:1 at about 3.55MHz. Bringing it down to a height of 10m makes this a lot worse (**Fig 5.14**).

At 7.1MHz (40m) you find that the match is better than 1.8:1 across the band. 10.12MHz (30m) is not so good at 28:1 (at a height of 20m), but 14MHz (20m) is far better at about 2:1, as is 18MHz (17m) at less than 2:1.

And so it goes on. In fact the anten-nas matches well at 24.9MHz (12m), 28.5MHz and even 50MHz (6m). Only 21MHz (15m) is a lit-tle bit of a fly in the ointment with an SWR of about 17:1.

This antenna is a good

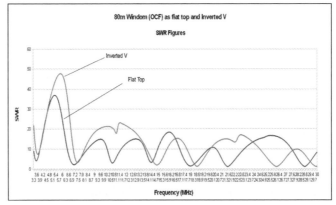

Fig 5.14:
Changing an 80m OCFD into an inverted V alters where it has a low SWR – try modelling it yourself

example of how running a whole series of measurements from 3.5–30MHz and then plotting them with Excel/OpenOffice Calc is a good way of seeing how it matches. With MMANA-GAL you can also play with the lengths, height and feed point position to see what effect it has on the antenna's performance. Go ahead and try it now.

Optimising the 40m OCFD with MMANA-GAL

The standard design for a 40m off centre fed dipole is that it should be 20.11m (66ft) long, fed at the one-third position 6.7m (22ft) with a 4:1 balun, where it will work on 40, 20 and 10m.

OK, so go ahead and open up the 40m OCFD file that I created for you. It is called 'OCFD_40.maa'. To get the antenna resonant in the middle of 40m, when mounted at 10m, I had to make it a little longer – actually 6.85m/13.7m for a total length of 20.55m. At 10m height you will also struggle to get the SWR down below about 1.8:1 with a 4:1 balun (**Fig 5.15**).

Now if you run this model at other frequencies you will see that you also get a good match at 14MHz (20m) and 28MHz (10m), which is in accordance with theory. But you will see that the match on 21MHz (15m) is not that good – I'll leave you to try it.

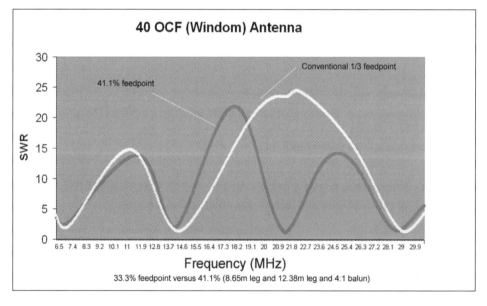

Fig 5.15: MMANA-GAL shows that moving the feed point on a 40m OCFD gains you another band

So can we do anything to help? Apparently we can. In MMANA-GAL try changing the two wires so that one is 8.65m and the other is 12.38m and run the calculations again. Now you will find that you also have a low SWR on 21MHz (15m), albeit at the expense of a slightly worse match on 40m.

Now, with the height at 10m I'll leave you to look at the far field plots and work out if you think this is an effective DX antenna on 20m and above when mounted at 10m. But the pattern is not that much different to the original OCFD design we looked at earlier – and you get an extra band for free.

The magnetic loop antenna

The magnetic loop is often touted as the ideal small antenna – it is tiny, can be made to work on a range of frequencies, will work well when mounted vertically at a low height, but has a very narrow bandwidth.

I have designed a model of an HF mag loop for you to play with (**Fig 5.16**). It is called 'Mag_loop__80cm_20m_vertical.maa' and is pretty much what it says. The loop is 80cm in diameter and the file is set up to work on a frequency of 14.010MHz exactly, using a capacitor value of 53.65 pF to bring it to resonance, when mounted at height of 10m.

If you run the program at 14.010MHz you will see that the antennas has an SWR of 1.07:1 Looking at the SWR plot you will see that it is very high Q. That is, it has a very narrow bandwidth.

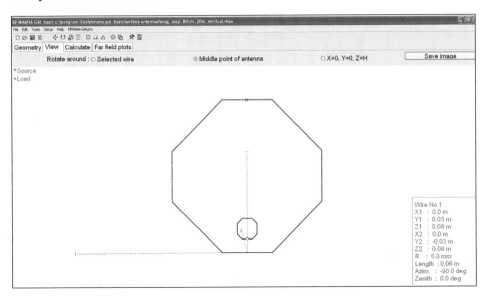

Fig 5.16:
The magnetic loop can be modelled as an octagon, which is quite tricky to build in MMANA-GAL

Looking at the far field plots you will see that, when mounted at any height up to about 10m it is a little bit of a cloud warmer (high angle), but in fact it seems to perform reasonably well even when mounted at 1m above ground.

I'll leave you to play with different heights to see what effects you get.

You can also 'tune' the capacitor for other bands. You can get the program to do this automatically for you, For example, set the frequency to 28.5MHz and run it. You will get an SWR of about 3217:1. Now go to the 'Optimization' option, set the SWR option to the right and the others to the left (to optimise SWR and ignore the other parameters).

Finally go the first line of the 'Parameters', change to 'Type' to 'Load' and set 'What' to 'C'. Now press start and MMANA-GAL will whirr away until it finds a match. At this point, if all has gone well you will find that it has selected a capacitance of 9.45 pF, which gives an SWR low of about 20.5:1.

But we can do better than that. Looking at the 'Plots' >> 'SWR' >> 'Detailed' view we can see that the low is actually at 28.6MHz – when we ran the optimisation routine it wasn't fine enough to go through every single frequency option.

Going back to 'Calculate' and running with 28.6MHz as the selected frequency shows the SWR is 2.3:1. That will do. I'll leave you to find out what the capacitance should be for 18MHz, 21MHz and 24MHz.

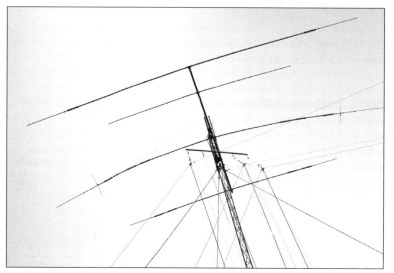

So we can use MMANA-GAL to work out what size variable capacitor we would need to resonate an 80cm magnetic loop from 14-29.7MHz. We can also look at the radiation patterns and confirm the theory that the loop will work at low heights and that the radiation pattern at low elevation angles is in the plane of the loop with nulls off the side (check the elevation pattern with 10 degrees selected).

Fig 5.17: MMANA-GAL can also be used to model beam antennas

Beam Antennas – HF and VHF

So far we haven't looked at how MMANA-GAL can handle beam antennas. The program comes with a whole host of designs for you to play with. Or, of course, you can design your own. Let's take a look at three of the supplied designs.

4-element 20m beam (Fig 5.17)

This can be found at ANT >>HF Beams >>4EL20HM.MAA. It uses a hairpin match to provide a 50 Ohm feed point as well as tapered aluminium tubing.

If you go to the View tab and zoom in you will be able to see the hairpin match. As a hint, it is built from wires 7, 8 and 9 and basically loops over the feed point on wire 5.

Wires 7 and 8 are both 36cm long and the hairpin match is only 10cm across.

Nevertheless, it provides the antenna with a good match – about 1.13:1 at 14.05MHz. The bandwidth of the antenna is also good with the SWR below 3:1 across the band.

If you don't get these results check that you have 'real life' ticked as my file opened with the antenna in 'free space'.

It looks like the design has been optimised for the CW end of the 20m band as the low point is very low at 14.05MHz. As an exercise you could play with the lengths to move the SWR minimum up into the middle of the band.

In terms of gain, the antenna appears to max out at about 13.7 dBi. At 20m it also has a low radiation angle of about 13 degrees. The front-to-back ratio, which is equally important with beams, is also excellent Using the 'Gain/FB' plots you can see how the gain and front/back are linked.

This shows how Yagi beam design is often about compromises – what do you want to maximise, gain or front-to-back? Or do you try to get the best of both worlds? And if you do, what happens to the antenna's bandwidth?

You can also try to raise and lower the design to see what happens to both the radiation pattern and also the elevation angle. Lowering it to 10m, for example, results in the maximum radiation angle increasing to about 25 degrees. While raising the height to 30m (which is probably about as high as a radio amateur is likely to achieve) causes the pattern to break up into multiple lobes.

What is clear is that this is a large antenna (with a 10m wingspan) and it certainly needs some height to make it work at its best.

20m HB9CV

If you don't have enough room for that four-element monster you could always try this two-element design from HB9CV. More usually found as a VHF antenna, the HB9CV uses a gamma match and a capacitor at the feed point to bring the match to 50 Ohms.

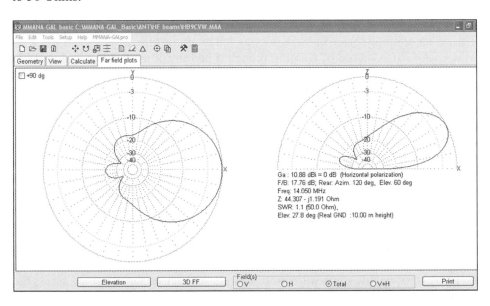

Fig 5.18: The HB9CV offers useful gain and a good front to back ratio

To see the design open ANT >>HF Beams >>HB9CVW.MAA.

While the HB9CV design also has a wingspan of about 10m, it is actually very short – with a boom length of 2.65m. Nevertheless, the design manages to give a peak forward gain of about 11.8 dBi and a front-to-back ratio of about 15-16 dB (**Fig 5.18**).

Again, make sure that you select 'Real' ground before running the calculation. As another exercise you might want to see if you can redesign the antenna for two metres (145MHz). I would start by creating the two elements and sizing the boom length accordingly. Then you can add in the matching network. Good luck!

2m two-element Moxon beam

Fig 5.19:
*The 2m Moxon
offers excellent
front to back
and useful gain*

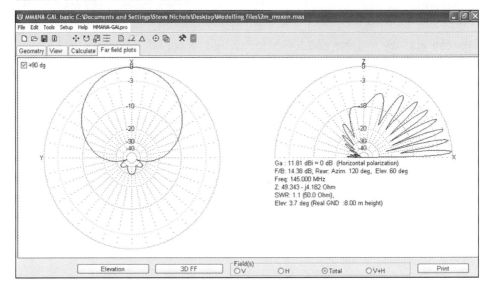

This is an antenna that I know works as I have built one, after modelling it in MMANA-GAL. A word of warning though, I had to cut mine down dramatically from the calculated dimensions to get it to resonate on 2m. I think this was again due to the use of PVC-coated wire and its reduced velocity factor.

To see the design open up the supplied file 2m_Moxon.maa (**Fig 5.19**).

I am indebted to AB1JX who has an online calculator, which can not only calculate the dimensions for a Moxon antenna, but can also generate the MMANA-GAL .mma file too. See http://ab1jx.webs.com/calcs/moxon/index.html

As you can see the model only consists of six wires. The physical construction is quite easy and as you can see from the photograph I made mine from PVC tubing as bought from a hardware store. The joints were also bought and the whole thing was glued together with PVC cement. I used a SO239 for the cable connection and glued the two side elements into a plastic drinking straw (once I had it set up correctly). To provide some waterproofing I also used heat-shrink tubing across the straw and part of the wire.

This little antenna works very well. I have used it in a couple of two metre contests and have worked well over 250 miles with it. It is so light that it can be held aloft on a 10m fishing pole, although I only use the first eight metres or so of the pole due to the top not being very strong.I rotate it by hand after using bungee cords to secure it to a wooden fence. The performance is not much different to an HB9CV design, giving a peak of 11.9 dBi of forward gain and 14.38 dB front-to-back.

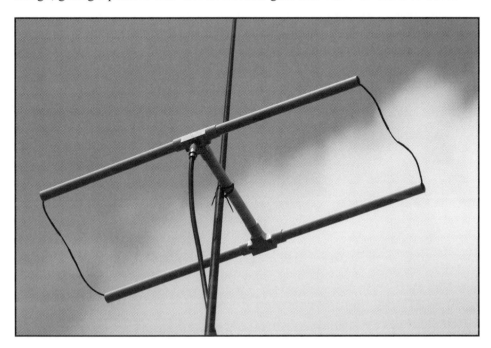

Fig 5.20:
The little 2m Moxon can easily be supported on a fishing pole

The Moxon (**Fig 5.20**), however, is easier to build than an HB9CV with fewer components and a simplified feed point.

You can easily scale the Moxon beam up for the HF bands, as long as you build it properly. Why not try designing and modelling a 10m version? If you get stuck the dimensions are available on the internet.

Conclusion

Well, the aim of this chapter was to introduce you to some of the designs supplied with MMANA-GAL and also some of my own. I wanted you to see how practical the program is and how it can be worth its weight in gold in terms of making sure everything works the way it should before you start building an antenna properly.

In addition to the antennas you have read about here, I have also used MMA-NA-GAL to model and then build a 10m Slim Jim made out of 450 Ohm ribbon cable, plus a 2m version using 300 Ohm ribbon cable.

Once the correct velocity factors of the cables were ascertained it was relatively easy to then take the measurements, shorten the design and then build it.

Plus a lot of antennas that I have tested for the RSGB's 'RadCom' magazine have also been modelled in MMANA-GAL to get a better idea of how they work – or in some cases don't. There was one antenna submitted for review that didn't work well at all, with a very poor SWR and even worse DX potential. When modelled it turned out that it behaved pretty much as the MMANA-GAL model said it would!

I hope that this has encouraged you to get started with MMANA-GAL and that you now have the confidence to use the software properly. If you get stuck it is often easier to start with an existing design and modify it. And as I said earlier, it can often help if you sketch out your design, and more importantly the dimensions, on a piece of paper first before you start to build it in MMANA-GAL.

6

MMANA-GAL Limitations

MMANA-GAL is pretty much a 'miracle' program and absolutely free. Having said that, it does have a few limitations, some of which may never bother you. But it is worth knowing what they are.

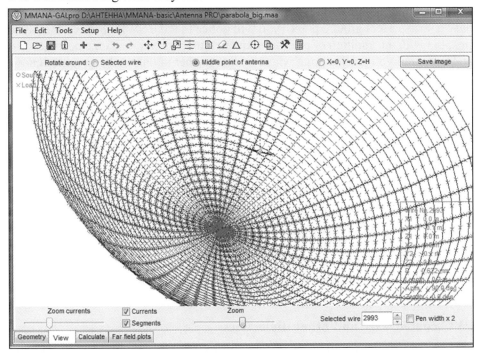

Fig 6.1:
If you want to build struc-tures like this parabolic dish you will need to upgrade to MMANA-GAL PRO

Limits

The basic version of MMANA-GAL has a limit of 8,192 segments and 512 wires. To be honest, this is probably more than enough for most people. You can build most common ham radio antennas within the limits. It is really only when you are modelling very intricate antennas (segments) or building models of large conduct-ing structures (wires) that you could come unstuck.

If that is the case the PRO version (**Fig 6.1**) of MMANA-GAL can come to the rescue.

Ground

As specified earlier, MMANA-GAL cannot model buried radials. Only NEC4-based modelling programs can handle this as it contains the code for computing how these behave.

NEC-2 does not permit wires either on or below ground. Antenna guru, the late LB Cebik W4RNL, wrote that radial systems must be constructed above ground, usually at a minimum height of about 0.001 wavelength. Adding that NEC-2 also recommends limiting the number of wires at a junction to about 30, making a 32-radial system about the largest that is practical.

You may notice with MMANA-GAL that adding successive radials to a vertical doesn't always result in lowering of an antenna's SWR. In real life, if you mount a quarter-wave vertical on a ground post only you will have significant ground losses. Adding radials will reduce the feed point impedance until such time as you have a near-perfect ground plane (you will notice that the SWR changes quickly at first, but with the addition of each subsequent radial the SWR change becomes less and less, until you reach a point where adding further radials makes no difference).

LB Cebik did a lot of work with NEC-2 modelling and the way it treats radials. If you are likely to model vertical antennas it might be worth having a look at his analysis at: *http://www.antennex.com/w4rnl/col0501/amod39.htm*

Surroundings

MMANA-GAL cannot model the surroundings of the antenna. That is, houses, trees, sheds, metal guttering, fences and the rest.

To be honest, this is not a limitation that is unique to MMANA-GAL – other modelling programs suffer from the same problem. However, in practice, the results of modelling horizontal HF antennas at elevation heights of 5-10m or more are generally in accordance with real life, as long as the antenna is in the clear and doesn't have any significant conducting objects within about a wavelength or so of the structure.

PVC-coated wire and other dielectrics

MMANA-GAL does a good job of modelling copper, aluminium and iron tubing and wire. But as mentioned throughout the book it can't handle dielectrics. That is, plastic-coated wire or coated open wire feeder needs special attention. Your designs will assume that you are using bare wire, but in reality the velocity factor of your wire could be much lower than unity.

The net effect is that your physical antennas will have to be smaller than the model suggests to resonate where you want them to.

This could be as small as five per-cent smaller for a simple dipole (taking into account end effects too), or much more if you are using ribbon cable. Some 300 Ohm ribbon in a design I used had a velocity factor of about 89%, while some 450 Ohm cable came out at a measured 78%.

The rule is, if it is a single element antenna like a dipole, build it to the size MMANA-GAL suggests and then cut or fold back until you get the desired effect. If it is a multi-element antenna I would steer clear of PVC-coated wire where possible, or just reduce each wire by a few per cent at a time until you get to where you need to be.

Remember, it is easier to cut wire than it is to add it back on!

Other limitations

MMANA-GAL doesn't allow you to assign a user-specified material conductivity or resistivity to the model wires, frequency compensation, or close-wire compensation. For a beginner (who this manual is aimed at) these are not massive problems.

MMANA-GAL PRO

The PRO version MMANA-GAL is a powerful antenna-analysing tool that was developed around the successful, but basic, MMANA-GAL engine.

To maintain compatibility with existing files much of the original MMANA-GAL functionality has been incorporated into the new software. But the PRO version has been specifically developed to handle very complex antenna designs.

To give a comparison:

Parameters	PRO version	Basic version
Segments (max)	up to 32000 (16GB RAM)	8192
Wires (max)	3000	512
Sources (max)	200	64
Loads (max)	300	100
Merged antenna files	2 to 4	none
Undo/Redo	unlimited	none
Auto check wires	yes	none

This kind of functionality allows you to build elaborate structures, such as microwave dishes or even car or aircraft bodies. As such it is a more professional tool than the basic MMANA-GAL, which will probably suffice for the vast majority of hams.

A personal licence for MMANA-GAL PRO costs approx $99 (at the time of publishing). See the author's website at *http://dl2kq.de/promm/*

Other Antenna Modelling Programs

There are lots of antenna modelling programs on the market, although many are aimed at professional RF engineers, with price tags to match. Here we look at a few packages that are best suited to radio amateurs.

EZNEC v5

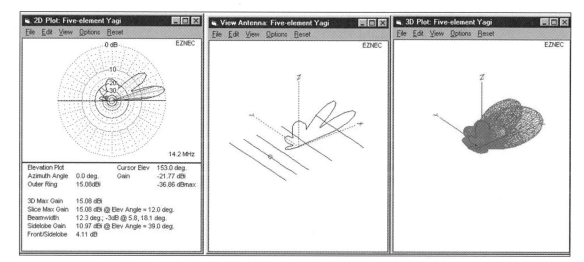

Fig 7.1:
*EZNEC has a
loyal following,
especially in
the US*

EZNEC is probably the best known of the antenna modelling packages for radio hams, although it is not free. Produced by Roy Lewallen, W7EL, it is a great program with a loyal following.

EZNEC v5, the basic version of the NEC-2 programs, offers 3-D plots with 2-D slicing, ground-wave output, stepped diameter correction, and numerous short-cuts to antenna geometry modification.

EZNEC plots azimuth and elevation patterns; tells you gain, feed point impedance, SWR, and current distribution; finds and reports beam width, 3-dB pattern points, f/b ratio, take-off angle, side-lobe characteristics; and more.

All information, including patterns, can be displayed on screen or printed on any Windows-compatible printer. Antenna descriptions and pattern plots are easily saved and recalled for future analysis. Multiple patterns can be superimposed on a single graph for comparison. See the pattern and antenna currents on the same colour 3-D display (**Fig 7.1**) as the antenna. Rotate the antenna display and zoom in for details.

As well, there are new facilities for entering traps and considerable annotation capabilities. Standard EZNEC is restricted to 500 segments. EZNEC Plus (see below) offers additional wire construction and movement capabilities, along with higher segment limits.

EZNEC costs $89, although there is a free demo version. With the EZNEC v. 5.0 demo program, you'll be able to see exactly how EZNEC v. 5.0 works, what it does - and doesn't - do, and how it's used. That's because it's a full EZNEC v. 5.0 program with all features and complete on-line manual. The only difference between the demo and standard programs is that the demo program allows only 20 segments, which limits the complexity of antenna you can analyse.

See *http://www.eznec.com*

EZNEC+ v5 and Pro

EZNEC+ has all the features of the standard program, plus:

- 1,500 segments vs 500 for the standard program - allowing very complex antennas to be analysed
- Circular polarisation far field analysis in addition to the linear polarisation capability of the standard program
- Double-precision calculating engine in addition to the standard mixed-precision engine
- Easy importation of wire coordinates (GW lines) from NEC-format files
- Additional SWR sweep displays: Smith chart, return loss, and reflection coefficient magnitude
- 10,000 frequency sweep steps vs 1,000 for the standard program
- Writes input files for IONCAP/VOACAP propagation programs
- Additional wire duplication and manipulation features.

There are two professional (EZNEC Pro) programs, EZNEC Pro/2 and EZNEC Pro/4. They are identical except that EZNEC Pro/4 can use NEC-4 for calculations as well as the NEC-2 used by the other EZNEC program types.

In addition to the features of EZNEC+, the professional programs include:

- 20,000 segment capability (vs 500 for EZNEC and 1,500 for EZNEC+)
- Ground wave analysis (of interest mostly to AM broadcasters)
- Automated rectangular wire grid creation
- Loss can be included in wire insulation
- The ability to read and write files in NEC format
- Plane wave excitation
- 100,000 frequency sweep steps.

The primary advantages of NEC-4 are that buried conductors can be modelled, and NEC-4 is relatively free of the small error produced by NEC-2 when analysing connected wires of different diameters.

EZNEC Pro/2 costs approx $500 and EZNEC Pro/4 is approx $650.

Purchasers of EZNEC Pro/4 must first obtain an NEC-4 license. At the time of writing, NEC-4 prices range from $300 for a US non-commercial or educational license to $1,500 for a non-U.S. commercial license.

However, prices change, so please consult the LLNL NEC-4 web site https://ipo. llnl.gov/?q=technologies-software-browse_software-app&s=NEC for current information.

For more information about EZNEC Pro, see *http://www.eznec.com*

4nec2

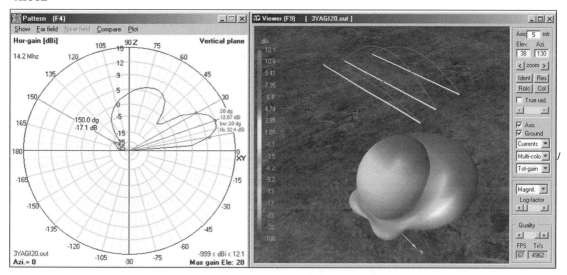

4nec2 is a free Nec2, Nec4 and windows-based tool for creating, viewing, optimising and checking 2D and 3D style antenna geometry structures. It can also generate, display and/or compare near/far-field radiation patterns for both novice and experienced antenna modellers (**Fig 7.2**).

Fig 7.2: 4nec2 can also generate, display and/or compare near and far-field radiation patterns

When running frequency sweeps, linear or logarithmic-style SWR, gain, F/B-ratio and impedance line-charts are produced. With the included optimiser and sweeper one is able to optimise antenna – and/or other environment-variables for gain, resonance, SWR, efficiency and/or F/B, F/R-ratio.

With the sweeper you can also graphically display the effect of changing one or more of these variables for a specified range of values/frequencies.

For the novice, a graphically-based 3D geometry-editor is included that requires no additional NEC knowledge, while still enabling you to create and visualise and compare current-distribution, far/near-field patterns and gain/SWR charts.

More experienced modellers can use the gradient style and/or the genetic algorithm based optimisers to improve their designs. Unlike the Nec-2 engine, the Nec-4 engine is not (yet) public-domain software and a license is needed to use it. A Nec-4 licence is available from the Lawrence Livermore National Laboratory.

For more details see http://www.qsl.net/4nec2/

MININEC Pro

Fig 7.3: MININEC Pro is also available for Linux and Mac computers

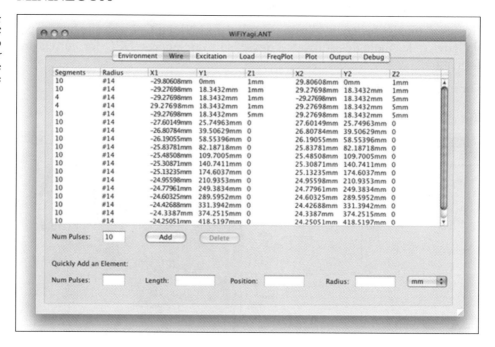

MININEC Pro is an antenna analysis program for Windows, Linux and Macintosh (**Fig 7.3**) computers from Black Cat Systems. Any type of antenna may be analysed. The physical design of the antenna is entered (such as the lengths of wires and elements). For a given frequency, the feed point impedance is calculated, along with theoretical efficiency.

Plots of the radiation patterns may also be displayed and printed.

One added bonus with MININEC Pro is that it is available for the Mac and Linux platforms as well as Windows.

The cost is approx $29 (for the download version) and approx $39 (for the CD-ROM version).

For more details see http://www.blackcatsystems.com

Appendix
Using the Supplied CD-ROM

The attached CD will auto-start in most PCs but if it doesn't clicking on index.htm will start the interface. The CD is broken down into four sections

- MMANA-GAL Software
- Other Example Antennas
- Antenna Software
- Other Software

MMANA-GAL Software

This is a zip file. Once the software is installed it creates a directory called ANT with many examples of MMANA-GAL designs. Some of these are referenced in the book.

Other Example Antennas

The disk contains a number of sample .maa files that are referenced in the book and will help with your understanding of how to use the software. These files can be opened off the CD-ROM from within the MMANA-GAL software or can be saved to your hard drive. Clicking on them via the CD-ROM's does not open them in MMANA-GAL, although you can save them from here. These files are also available online at:

http://www.infotechcomms.net/downloads/MMANAGAL_samples.zip

Antenna Software

Also on the disk are examples of other antenna modelling programs. These include:

EZNEC v5.0 – a demonstration version from *www.eznec.com*

MININEC Pro (Windows) - An antenna analysis program from Black Cat Systems. Also available for Linux and Macintosh *www.blackcatsystems.com*

4nec2 - A free tool for creating, viewing, optimising and checking 2D and 3D style antenna geometry structures. *www.qsl.net/4nec2*

Additional information on these programs can be found on their relevant web sites.

Other Software

Over 30 amateur radio software packages are included on the Software CD along with other programmes that may be useful to radio amateurs. Fuller descriptions of the software included can also be found on the CD. Included are:

AALog - A comprehensive logger and eQSL.cc compatible.

AGW Software – includes

AGW Packet

AGW Tracker

AGW Monitor

AGW DX Robot

AGW DX Net Manager

AGW DX QSL

Airlink Express - digital mode software

Amateur Contact Log – A logging program

Contest Trainer – A contest trainer produced by G4FON

CW Decoder - Translate Morse code to printed text

CwGet - A program to decode Morse code

CW Player - A program to learn and train the Morse code

CW Skimmer - CW decoder and analyser

CwType - A terminal program for CW operators

DX Lab - is a suite of interoperating applications, including:

Commander

DXKeeper

DXLab Launcher

DXView

Pathfinder

PropView

SpotCollector

WinWarbler

Great Circle Map - Produce your own Great Circle map

Ham Radio Deluxe - Version 6 is an integrated suite of software.

Jason Mode - A weak signal communication program

MMSSTV - For transmitting and receiving SSTV

MMTTY - RTTY software program.

MMVARI - Sound card program for RTTY-PSK-FSK-MFSK

Morse Runner - Contest simulator

Morse Trainer - Morse trainer produced by G4FON.

Multi PSK - Multimode program by F6CTE

N1MM Logger - Contest logging program

QSL Maker - Print your own QSL cards

Sat Explorer - Satellite tracking and antenna positioning

Sat Scape - Satellite tracking program

SD - Fast and simple contest logging

Simplex - Repeater software

WinDRM - Amateur Radio Digital Voice

WinGrid - IARU QTH Locator grid square distance and bearing calculator. Includes:

    RF Safety Calculator

    Power Loss/dB Calculator

    Solar/Lunar Tracking Program

    P3T AO-40 Telemetry Program

    IPS Emulator for Windows

WSJT - For weak-signal digital communication by amateur radio

MAP65 – A wideband receiver for JT65 signals

WSPR - Weak Signal Propagation Reporter for MF and HF bands

SimJT - Generates JT65 and CW test signals

Non Amateur Radio Programs that may be useful

Apache Open Office - A free and indispensable office Suite.

Note: this has been specifically included as you may find the Calc option invaluable for creating the MMANA-GAL graphs of SWR v frequency detailed in the book.

Adobe Reader XI – PDF file reader

Doro PDF Writer - Creates PDFs

PDF-XChange Viewer - An alternative to Adobe's Acrobat Reader

IMPORTANT NOTE:

Please note this software is supplied with no warranty or implied approval by the Radio Society of Great Britain. The producers of this CD have made no charge for the software listed below and provide no technical support for it. If you choose to use the software it is entirely at your own risk and you are bound by any conditions applied by the makers or their agents. The Radio Society of Great Britain will not accept any responsibility for losses or damage arising from the use of this software. The brief descriptions and information are from the maker's websites. We provide no installation instructions but all items are eithe zip or self-installing files.

Additional information about MMANA-GAL

MMANA-GAL is freeware. The world wide copyright is held by Makoto (Mako) Mori, JE3HHT. Programs are released with no support or warranty. The author accepts no responsible and/or liability for damage that may be caused by the use his program.

JE3HHT's software may be freely copied and/or re-distribution providing that you make no charge for the programs.

The original code was by JE3HHT - Makoto Mori

MMANA-GAL basic and MMANA-GAL Pro by DL1PBD - Alex Schewelew, and DL2KQ – Igor Gontcharenko.

Obtaining the latest version of MMANA-GAL

The latest version of MMANA-GAL is always available from http://hamsoft.ca. In addition, users have access to support directly from the MM Hamsoft website.

Yahoo Group

Additional support can be found on the MMANA-GAL Yahoo Group at http://groups.yahoo.com/group/MMANA-GAL/ and the MM-Hamsoft Yahoo Group at http://groups.yahoo.com/group/MM-HAMSOFT/

YouTube

Searching for MMANA-GAL on YouTube will result in you finding many helpful instructional videos about the software.